The Minitab Manual

Dorothy Wakefield • Kathleen McLaughlin

STATISTICS
Informed Decisions
Using Data

Michael Sullivan III

PEARSON

Prentice
Hall

Upper Saddle River, NJ 07458

Editor-in-Chief: Sally Yagan
Supplement Editor: Joanne Wendelken
Assistant Managing Editor: John Matthews
Production Editor: Wendy A. Perez
Supplement Cover Manager: Paul Gourhan
Supplement Cover Designer: Joanne Alexandris
Manufacturing Buyer: Ilene Kahn

© 2004 by Pearson Education, Inc.
Pearson Education, Inc.
Upper Saddle River, NJ 07458

Printed in the United States of America

10 9 8 7 6 5 4 3 2 1

ISBN 0-13-046497-X

Pearson Education Ltd., *London*
Pearson Education Australia Pty. Ltd., *Sydney*
Pearson Education Singapore, Pte. Ltd.
Pearson Education North Asia Ltd., *Hong Kong*
Pearson Education Canada, Inc., *Toronto*
Pearson Educación de Mexico, S.A. de C.V.
Pearson Education—Japan, *Tokyo*
Pearson Education Malaysia, Pte. Ltd.
Pearson Education, *Upper Saddle River, New Jersey*

▶ Introduction

The MINITAB Manual is one of a series of companion technology manuals that provide hands-on technology assistance to users of Sullivan *Statistics: Informed Decisions Using Data.*

Detailed instructions for working selected examples and problems from *Statistics: Informed Decisions Using Data* are provided in this manual. To make the correlation with the text as seamless as possible, the table of contents includes page references for both the Sullivan text and this manual.

All of the data sets referenced in this manual are found on the data disk packaged in the back of every new copy of Sullivan *Statistics: Informed Decisions Using Data.* If needed, the MINITAB files (.mtp) may also be downloaded from the texts' companion website at www.prenhall.com/Sullivan.

▶ Contents:

	Sullivan Statistics: Informed Decisions Using Data	The MINITAB Manual
	Page:	Page:
Chapter 10 Inferences on Two Samples		
Section 10.1		
Example 2 *Matched Pairs Data*	596	220
Problem 9	602	222
Problem 13	603	223
Section 10.2		
Example 1 & 2 *Testing a Claim Regarding Two Means*	610, 613	224
Problem 9	616	225
Section 10.3		
Example 1 *Testing a Claim Regarding Two Proportions*	622	226
Problem 11	629	228
Section 10.4		
Example 2 *Testing a Claim Regarding Two Standard Deviations*	637	229
Problem 19	642	231
Chapter 11 Chi-Square Procedures		
Section 11.1		
Example 3 *The Chi-Square Goodness-of-Fit Test*	660	232
Problem 7	664	235
Section 11.3		
Example 2 *The Chi-Square Independence Test*	681	237
Problem 7	689	239
Chapter 12 Least Squares Regression and ANOVA		
Section 12.1		
Examples 1-5 *Least Squares Regression*	706-716	240
Problem 11	720	244
Section 12.2		
Examples 1-2 *Confidence and Prediction Intervals*	725	247
Problem 5	727	249
Section 12.3		
Problem 5	742	250
Problem 7	743	252

	Sullivan Statistics: Informed Decisions Using Data Page:	The MINITAB Manual Page:
Chapter 13 Nonparametric Statistics		
Section 13.2		
Examples 3 *Testing for Randomness*	763	254
Problem 5	765	256
Section 13.3		
Examples 1 *One-sample Sign Test*	771	257
Problem 7	774	259
Section 13.4		
Example 1 *Performing a Wilcoxon Signed-rank Test*	779	260
Problem 15	784	262
Section 13.5		
Example 1 *Performing a Mann-Whitney Test*	790	263
Problem 9	795	264
Section 13.6		
Example 1 *The Spearman Rank Correlation Coefficient*	800	265
Problem 5	803	268
Section 13.7		
Example 1 *Performing a Kruskal-Wallis Test*	807	269
Problem 5	811	272

Getting Started with MINITAB

▸ Using MINITAB Files

MINITAB is a Windows-based Statistical software package. It is very easy to use, and can perform many statistical analyses. When you first open MINITAB, the screen is divided into two parts. The top half is called the Session Window. The results of the statistical analyses are often displayed in the Session Window. The bottom half of the screen is the Data Window. It is called a Worksheet and will contain the data.

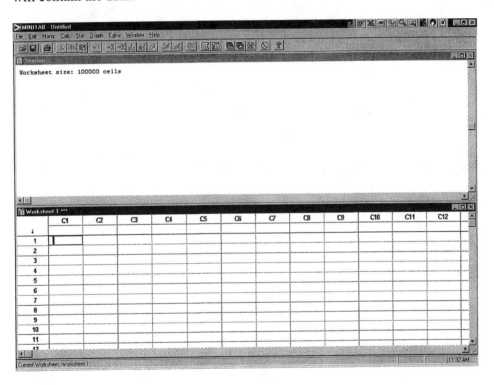

The data can either be entered directly into the Worksheet, or saved worksheets can be opened and used.

▶ Entering Data into the Data Window

To enter the data into the Data Window, you must first click on the bottom half of the screen to make the Data Window active. You can tell which half of the screen is active by the blue bar going across the screen. In the picture below, notice that the blue bar is in the middle of the screen, highlighting **Worksheet 1.** This indicates that the Data Window is active. The bar will be gray if the Window is not active. (Notice the Session Window bar is gray.)

In MINITAB, the columns are referred to as C1, C2, etc. Notice that there is an empty cell directly below each heading C1, C2, etc. This cell is for a column name. Column names are optional because you can refer to a column as C1 or C2, but a name helps to describe the data contained in a column. Enter the data beginning in cell 1. Notice that the cell numbers are located in the leftmost column of the worksheet.

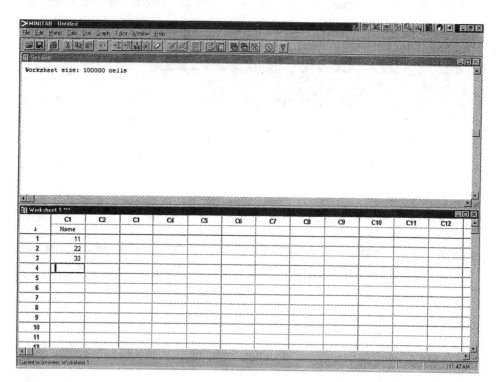

▸ Opening Saved Worksheets

Many of the worksheets that you will be using are saved on the enclosed data disk. To open a saved worksheet, click on **File → Open Worksheet.** The following screen will appear.

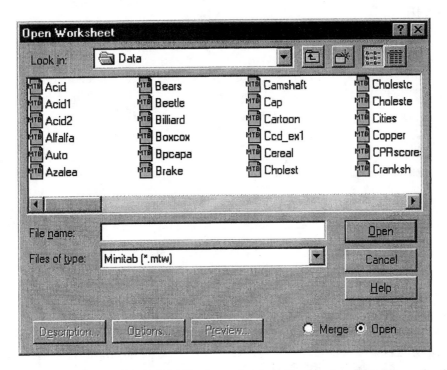

First, you must tell MINITAB where the data files are located. Since the data files are located on a CD data disk, you must tell MINITAB to **Look In** the CD drive. To do this, click on the down arrow to the right of the top input field and select the CD drive by double-clicking on it.

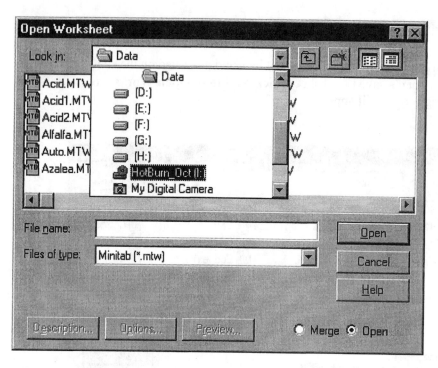

When you do this, you should see three folders listed. Select the MINITAB folder with a double-click. Now you should see a folder for each of the thirteen chapters of the book.

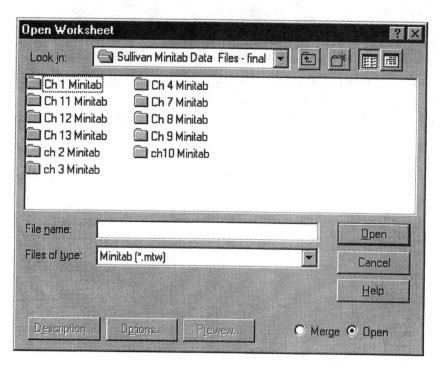

All data files are saved as MINITAB Portable worksheets and have the extension **.mtp.** Click on the down arrow for the field called **Files of type** and select **Minitab Portable (*.mtp).**

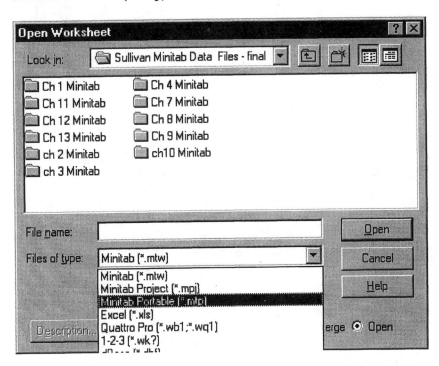

Now, select the folder called **Ch 1 Minitab** (by double-clicking) and you should see all the MINITAB worksheets for Chapter 1.

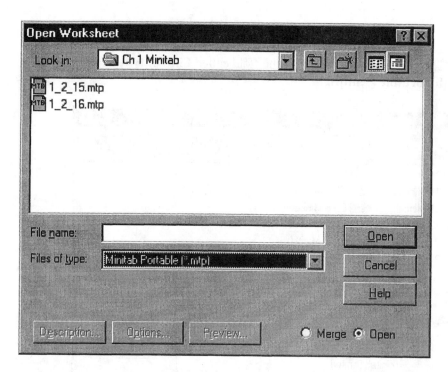

As you can see, **Ch 1** has only two worksheets saved on the CD. The naming
convention is as follows: the first number represents the chapter, the second
number represents the section of the chapter, and the third number represents the
problem number. For example, file **1_2_15** contains the data for problem 15 in
chapter 1 section 2. To open the worksheet **1_2_15**, double-click on it and the
worksheet should appear in the Data Window.

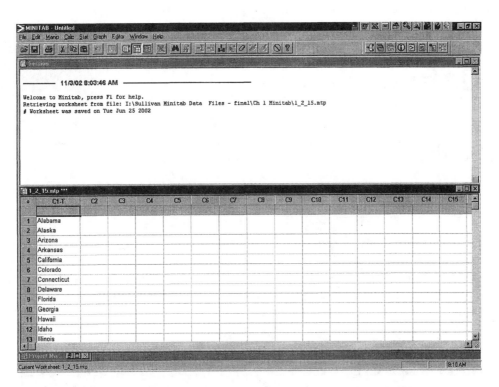

You are now ready to begin analyzing the data and learning more about MINITAB.

CHAPTER

Data Collection

1

Section 1.2

▶ Example 4 (pg. 18) Generating a Simple Random Sample

To select 10 residents randomly from the population of 8791, first you must represent each resident with a number. So, store the numbers 1 to 8791 in C1. Click on **Calc → Make Patterned Data → Simple Set of Numbers.** You should **Store patterned data in** C1. The numbers will begin **From the first value** 1 and go **To last value** 8791 **In steps of** 1.

Simple Set of Numbers	☒

S̲tore patterned data in: c1

F̲rom first value: 1

T̲o last value: 8791

I̲n steps of: 1

List each v̲alue 1 times

List the w̲hole sequence 1 times

Select

Help   O̲K   Cancel

Click on **OK** and the numbers 1 to 8791 should be in C1 of the Data Window.

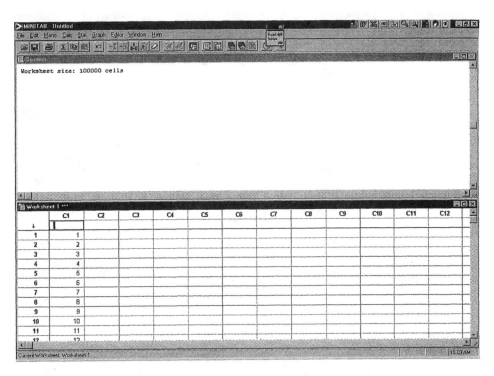

Next, you'd like to take a random sample of 10 residents. Since you do not want repeats, you will be sampling without replacement. This is the default type of sampling in MINITAB, so you won't have to do anything special for this sample. Click on **Calc → Random Data → Sample from columns.** You need to **Sample** 10 **rows from column** C1 and **Store the sample in** C2.

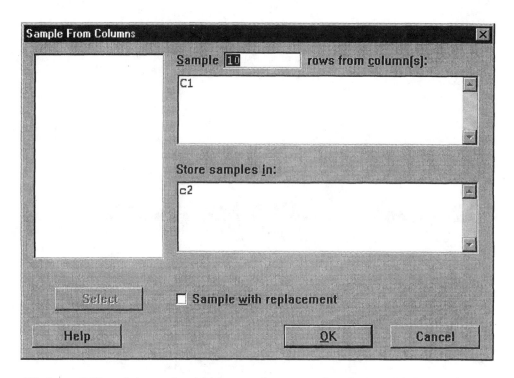

Click on **OK** and there should be a random sample of 10 resident numbers in C2.

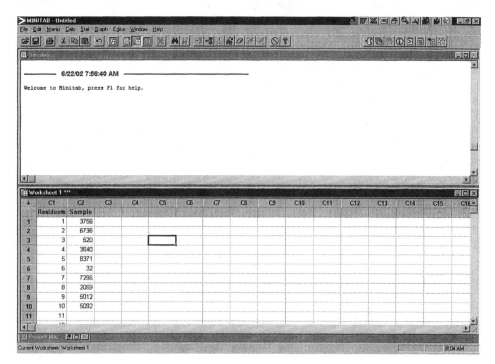

To order the sample list, click on **Manip** → **Sort.** You should **Sort column** C2 and **Store sorted column in** C3. You want to **Sort by column** C2.

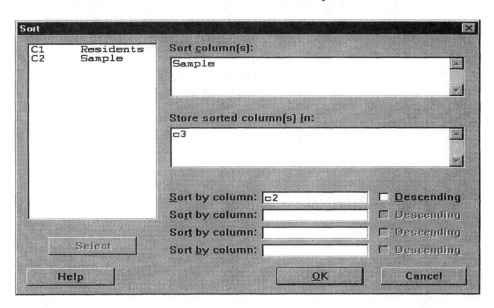

Click on **OK** and C3 should contain the sorted sample of 10 residents.

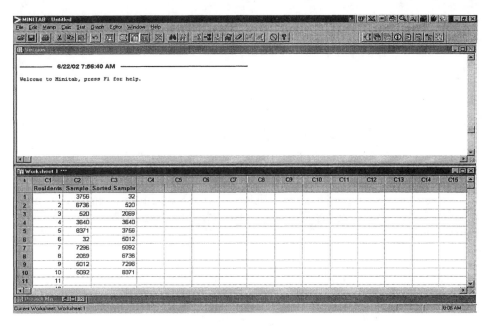

Since this is a *random* sample, each student will have different numbers in C2 and C3.

▶ Exercise 15 (pg. 19) Obtaining a Simple Random Sample

In this problem, notice that the 50 states are already numbered from 1 to 50. To select 10 states randomly from the 50, you need to store the numbers 1 to 50 in C1. Click on **Calc → Make Patterned Data → Simple Set of Numbers.** You should **Store patterned data in** C1. The numbers will begin **From the first value** 1 and go **To last value** 50 **In steps of** 1. Click on **OK** and the numbers 1 to 50 should be in C1 of the Data Window.

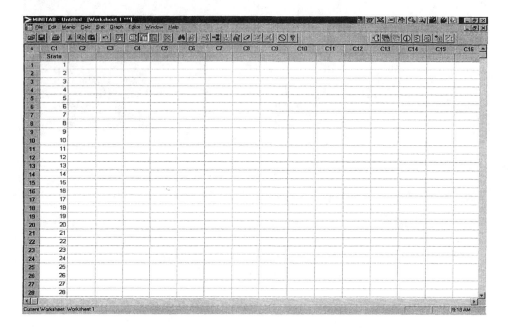

Next, to randomly sample 10 states, click on **Calc → Random Data → Sample from columns.** You need to **Sample** 10 **rows from column** C1 and **Store the sample in** C2.

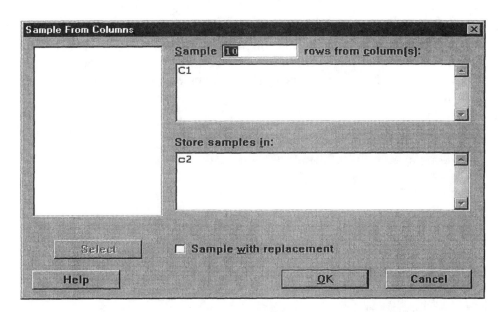

Click on **OK** and the sample of 10 state numbers should be in C2 of the Data
Window.

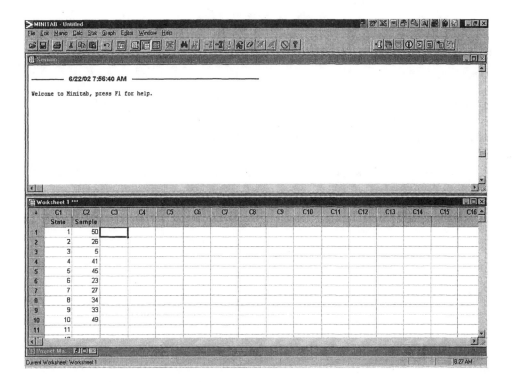

Finally, to order the sample list, click on **Manip → Sort.** You should **Sort column** C2 and **Store sorted column in** C3. You want to **Sort by column** C2. Click on **OK** and the sorted sample of 10 state numbers should be in C3 of the Data Window.

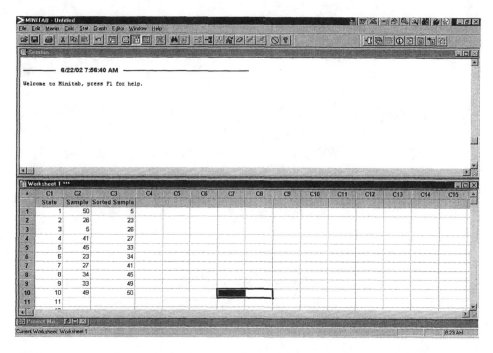

Look at your random sample above. Using the list of states on page 19 of your textbook, see which states are in this sample. From the list, you can see that State 5 is California, State 23 is Minnesota, State 26 is Montana, etc.

For part b of this exercise, repeat these steps to obtain a second random sample of size 10. You will get a different set of 10 states since your sample is random.

Organizing and Summarizing Data

CHAPTER

2

Section 2.1

▶ Example 3 (pg. 55) Constructing Frequency and Relative-
Frequency Bar Graphs, Pareto Charts

To create this bar chart, you will need to enter the data into the data worksheet.
It will be easier to make the chart if you use the two-letter abbreviation for each
of the states. In column 1, type in these abbreviations (as shown below). Label
the column by typing "State" in the gray cell in C1. Label column 2 "Frequency",
and type in the frequencies.

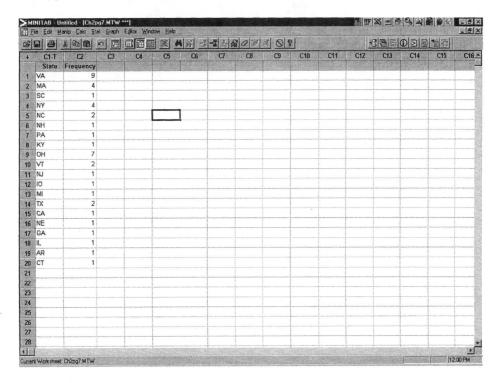

Next, calculate the relative frequencies. Since there are 43 presidents, you will
divide each frequency by 43. To do this, click on **Calc → Calculator.** You are

going to create a new column of relative frequencies, so we can name the column by entering "Relative Frequency" beside **Store result in variable:** as shown below. Next tell Minitab what you want to calculate. Click in the box beneath **Expression**, then type in **C2 / 43**. This tells Minitab to divide each value in C2 by 43.

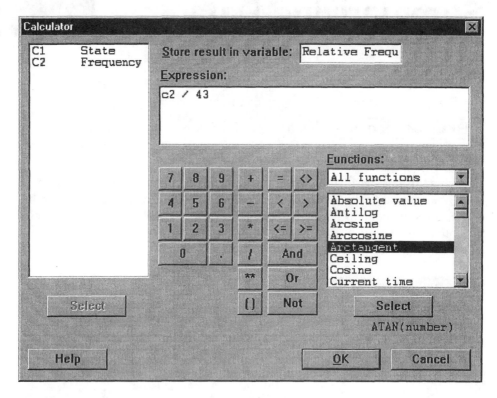

Click on **OK** and you should see the relative frequencies in C3.

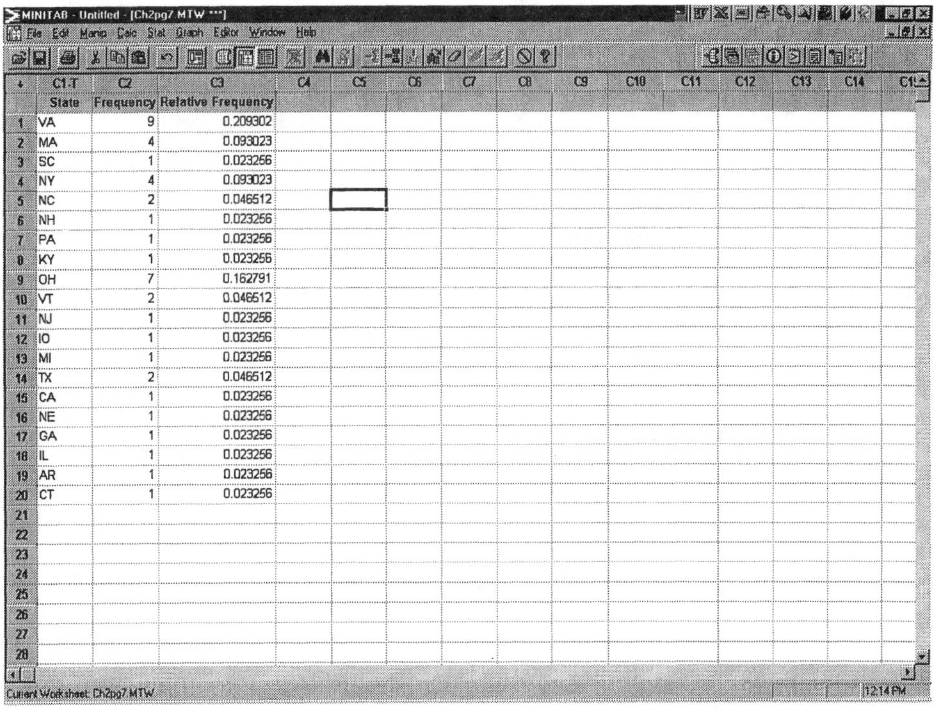

	C1-T State	C2 Frequency	C3 Relative Frequency
1	VA	9	0.209302
2	MA	4	0.093023
3	SC	1	0.023256
4	NY	4	0.093023
5	NC	2	0.046512
6	NH	1	0.023256
7	PA	1	0.023256
8	KY	1	0.023256
9	OH	7	0.162791
10	VT	2	0.046512
11	NJ	1	0.023256
12	IO	1	0.023256
13	MI	1	0.023256
14	TX	2	0.046512
15	CA	1	0.023256
16	NE	1	0.023256
17	GA	1	0.023256
18	IL	1	0.023256
19	AR	1	0.023256
20	CT	1	0.023256

Now you are ready to make the bar graph. Click on: **Graph → chart**. Now you must tell Minitab which variables to graph. Click in the field below "Y". The Y variable is the numerical measurement. In this case, it is our frequencies. Minitab is expecting a *column* here. Since C2 contains the frequencies, type in **C2**. The other way to do this is to notice that when you click on this field, a list of columns appears on the left side of the screen. You can select a column by double-clicking on it, or after a single click highlights the variable, click on **SELECT** at the bottom of the screen. Next click on the field below "X". Select **C1**, the state abbreviations.

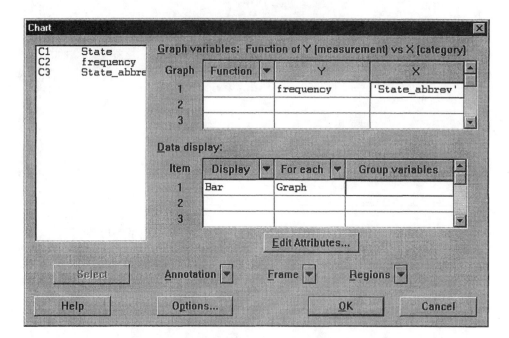

At this point, if you click on **OK**, MINITAB will draw a bar graph using default settings. Your graph will look like the one below.

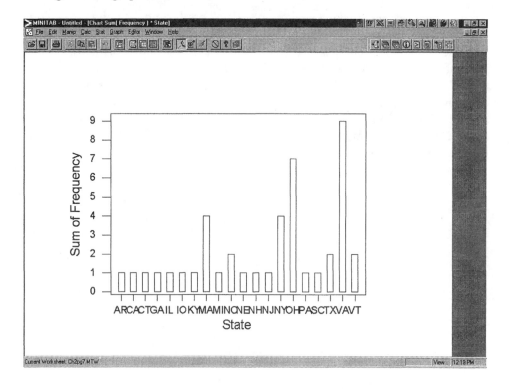

Notice the X-axis labels are not readable, there is no title on the graph, and the Y-axis label is "sum of frequency". We can instruct MINITAB to improve this chart, however. Close the Graph Window by clicking on the "X" in the upper right corner of the graph. Go back to the main Chart screen. (Click on: **Graph → chart**.) To label the X-axis "State" and the Y-axis "Frequency", click on: **Frame → Axis**. You should see the following screen.

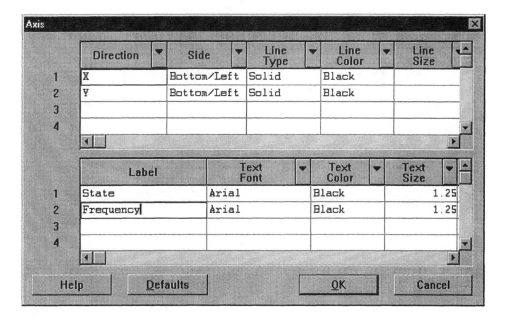

In the bottom half of the screen, beneath "Label" and beside "1", enter the label "State" for the X-axis. To do this, click on the word "Auto" and delete it, then type in the new label. In the next row, click on the word "Auto" and replace it with "Frequency".

Click on **OK** to close the screen. You will now be back to the main Chart screen.
Next, fix the lettering along the X-axis. The states will be much more readable if
we rotate the abbreviations by 90 degrees. To do this, simply click on **Frame** →
Tick and the following screen will appear. This screen looks very much like the
previous screen, but notice that the name in the top left corner of the blue bar is
"Tick".

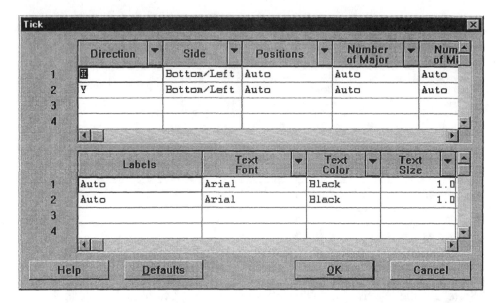

To rotate the labels for the tick marks, you must scroll over to right of the bottom
part of the screen. Use the right arrow to do this until you see **Text Angle.** Since
row 1 corresponds to the X-axis, enter **90** for a 90 degree rotation.

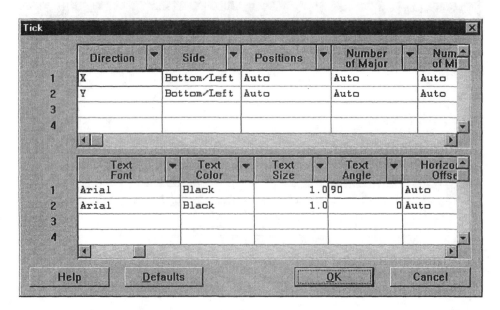

Click on **OK** to close the screen. You will now be back to the main Chart screen. The only thing left to do is to put a title on the chart. Click on **Annotation** → **Title** and enter an appropriate title in the first line of the screen.

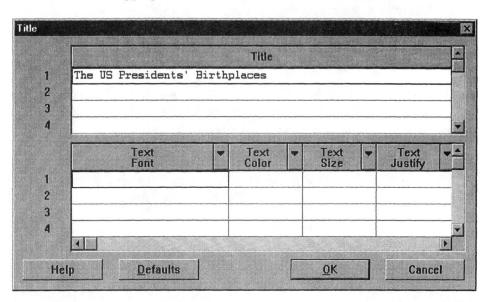

Click on **OK** twice and your chart should appear.

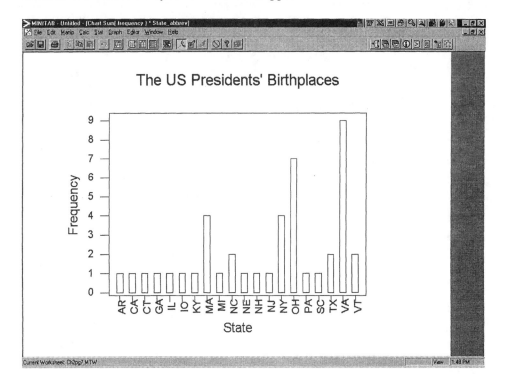

Notice that Minitab alphabetized the states so that your chart looks a little different than the one in the text. To print the graph, click on **File → Print Graph.** Next, click **OK** and the graph should print. Once the graph prints, click on the X in the upper right corner of the chart to close it.

To create a relative frequency bar chart, you just need to select the Relative Frequencies as the Y-axis variable. To make the chart, click on **Graph → chart.** This time, select C3 as the Y variable.

Minitab will still have all the settings that you used for the frequency bar chart, so the only other thing that you need to change is the Y axis label. Click on **Frame → axis.** Change the Y axis label to Relative Frequency.

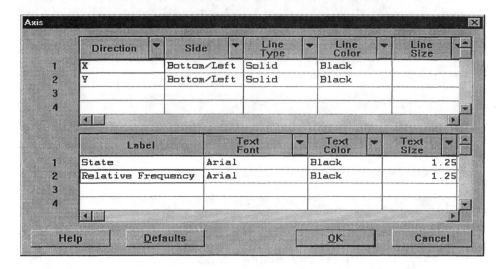

Click on **OK** twice and you should see the relative frequency bar chart.

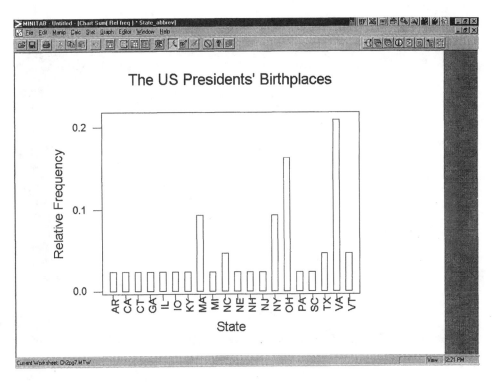

To create a Pareto chart, you simply need to tell Minitab to put the data in decreasing order. To do this, click on **Graph → Chart → Options.** Beneath **Order X Groups Based On**, click on **Decreasing Y.**

Click **OK** twice and the pareto chart should appear.

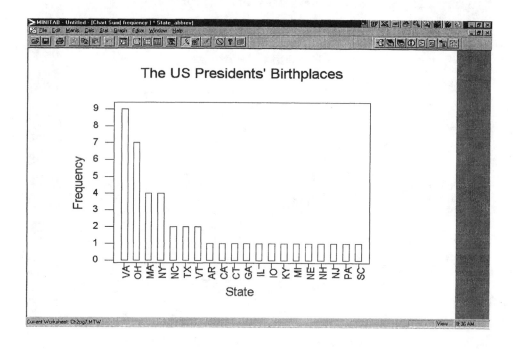

> ▸ Example 4 (pg. 57) Construct a side-by-side Bar Graph

Enter the data into a worksheet. Minitab is expecting this data to be in a
particular format. Minitab expects each row of data to consist of Education
Level, Relative Frequency and Year. Label C1 - C3 with those names. Since
Education Level is really an ordered variable -- it goes from lowest level to
highest level of education, we will number them as part of the title. If you don't
do this, Minitab will automatically alphabetize them. Now enter the data. Notice
that the Education Levels are repeated for the Year 2000 data.

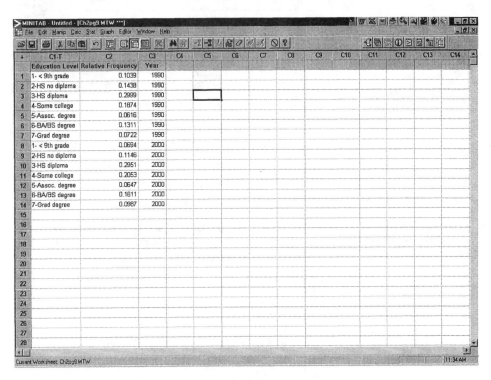

To make the graph Click on **Graph** → **chart**. Select **Relative Frequency** for the
Y variable and **Education Level** for the X variable. Click beneath **For Each** and
select **Group.** Click beneath **Group Variables** and select **Year.** This is telling
Minitab that the variable Year will separate our data into 2 groups.

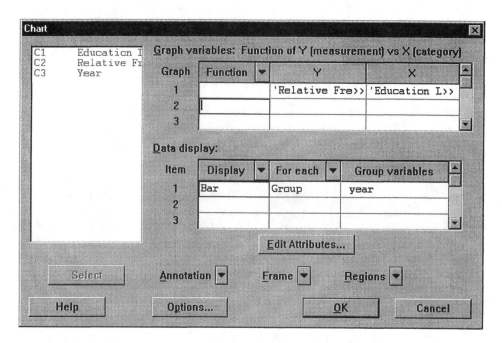

Next, tell Minitab that you want a side-by-side bar graph. Click on **Options**, and select **Cluster** and enter Year. Click on **OK**.

To add a title to the graph, click on **Annotation → Title.** Enter an appropriate title into Line 1.

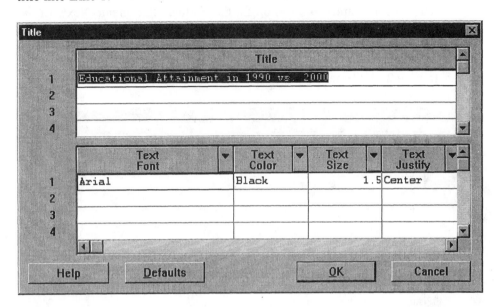

Click on **OK**, and you will be back to the main Chart screen. Now rotate the X-axis data labels. To do this, click on **Frame → Tick.** Beneath **Label** in the bottom half of the screen, scroll over to **Text Angle** and type **30** into Line 1 for the X-axis.

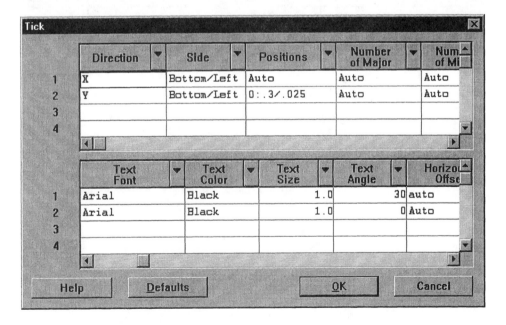

Continue to scroll to the right until you see both **Horizontal Placement**and **Vertical Placement.**   Use the down arrow to select **To the Left of** for the Horizontal Placement and **Centered on** for the Vertical Placement. Next, set the Y-axis tick marks so that you will be able to read the chart easier. Since the relative frequencies are small numbers, the tick marks should start at 0 and go up to 0.30. It would be nice if they have a spacing of 0.025. In the top half of this screen, in Line 2 and beneath **Positions**, type in 0 : .3 / .025.

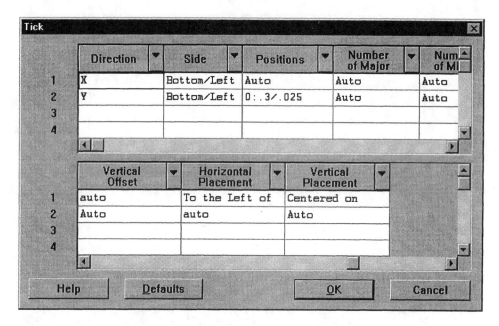

Click on **OK** twice and you should see the side-by-side chart.

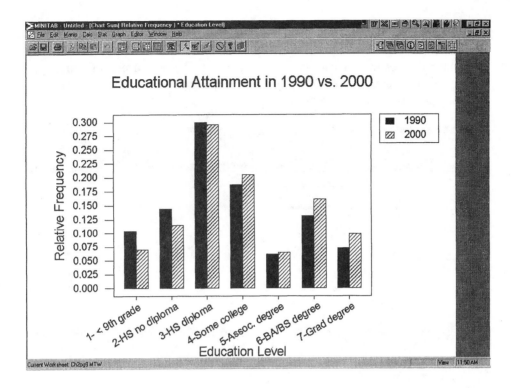

▶ Example 5 (pg.59)   Constructing a Pie Chart

This example uses the Educational Attainment data that was used in Example 4.
It uses only the data for Year 2000. However, this time you will need to enter the
frequencies, rather than the relative frequencies.

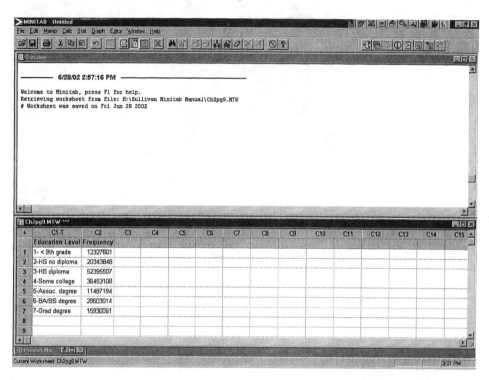

To create a Pie chart, click on **Graph → Pie chart.** On the screen that appears,
select **Chart Table** by clicking on the small circle to the left of it. Fill in the
appropriate variables. Select C1 for **Categories In** and C2 for **Frequencies In**.
Type in an appropriate **Title.**

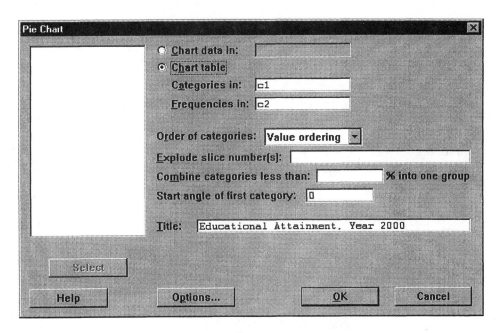

Click on **OK**, and the pie chart should appear.

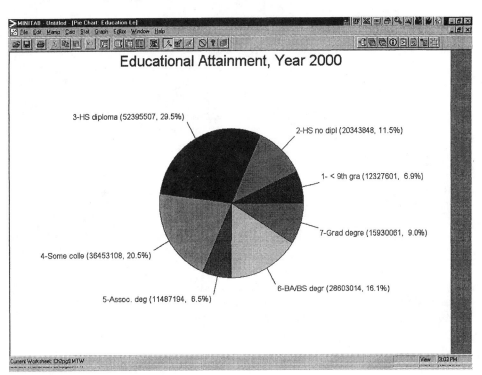

▶ Problem 15 (pg. 64) Construct relative frequency bar graphs

Open worksheet **ex2_1_15. (Note:** You may want to change the Education level titles so order and shorten them. One possibility is: 1-HS, no diploma, 2-HS diploma, 3-Some college, 4-Assoc degree, 5-BA/BS degree, 6-Grad degree. To change the titles, just type right over the ones in the worksheet.) First calculate relative frequencies for both Males and Females. To do this, click on **Calc**→ **Calculator.** To calculate the relative frequencies, you need to divide each frequency by the sum of the frequencies. This can be done in one step. If you **Store result in variable:** Male_RelFreq, this will give your new column an appropriate name. Enter the **Expression** "C2 / sum(C2)". This will divide each frequency by the sum of the frequencies in C2.

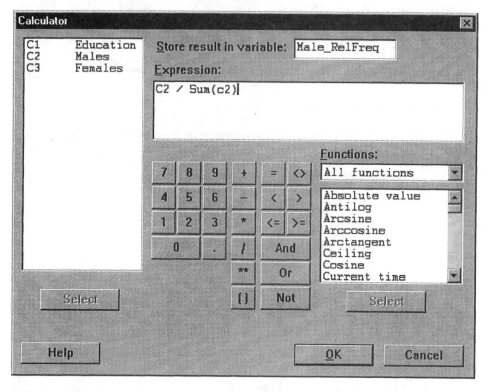

Click on **OK** and the relative frequencies should be in C4. Repeat this procedure to calculate the relative frequencies for Females. Name the new column "Female_RelFreq". The **Expression** will be "C3 / sum(C3)".

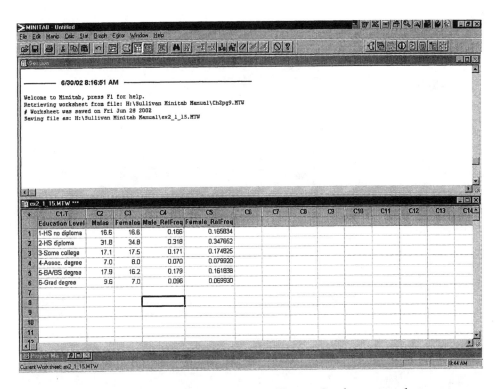

To make the bar graphs, click on **Graph → Chart**. On the screen that appears, select Male_RelFreq as the **Y-variable** and Education Level as the **X-variable.** Click on **Annotation → Title**, and enter an appropriate title in Line 1. Click on **OK.** Now rotate the X-axis tick mark labels since the Education levels are fairly long categories. Click on **Frame → Tick**. Use the same settings as you did in Example 4. In line 1 of the bottom portion of the screen, choose a **Text Angle** of **30** degrees. Continue to scroll to the right until you see both **Horizontal Placement** and **Vertical Placement.**   Use the down arrow to select **To the Left of** for the Horizontal Placement and **Centered on** for the Vertical Placement. Next, set the Y-axis tick marks so that you will be able to read the chart easier. Since the relative frequencies are small numbers, the tick marks should start at 0 and go up to 0.35. It would be nice if they have a spacing of 0.025. In the top half of this screen, in Line 2 and beneath **Positions**, type in 0 : .35 / .025.

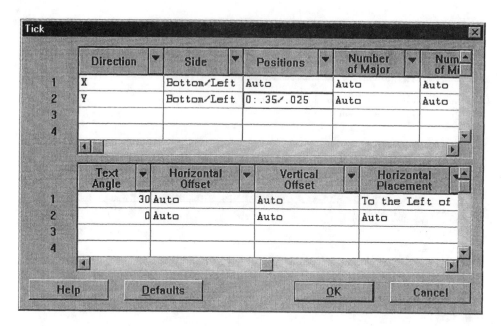

Click on **OK** twice to view the bar graph.

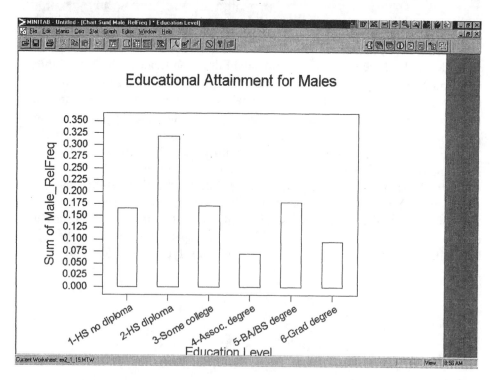

Repeat this procedure to create a bar for Females' educational attainment. Be
sure to change the Y-variable to "Female_RelFreq" and to change the **Title.** The
rest of the settings should still be set for you.

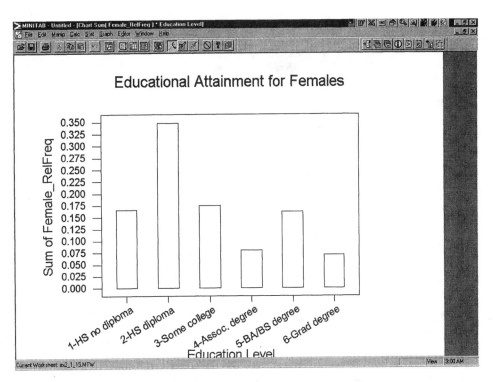

To create the side-by-side bar graph, you will need to set up the data in the proper format. Recall that Minitab was expecting both sets of data to be in one column. This is a simple procedure. We will create a new column that has the Education Level categories repeated for both males and females. You can do this using Cut and Paste or you can use Minitab's functions. To use Minitab's functions, click on **Manip → Stack → Stack columns.** Select C1 two times so that it appears twice in **Stack the following columns.** You'd like to **Store stacked data in** C6, so select **Column of current worksheet** and type in C6. Click on **OK**. To stack the relative frequencies, repeat this procedure. **Stack the following columns:** Male_RelFreq and Female_RelFreq. **Store stacked data in** C7. Click on **OK**.

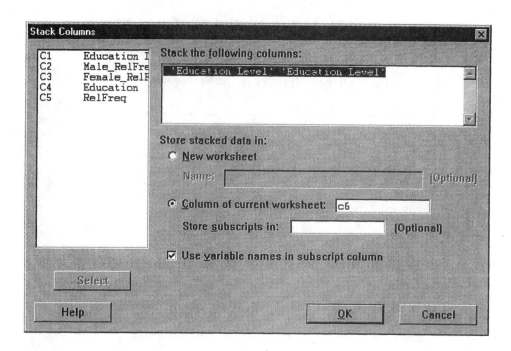

Name C6 and C7 appropriately. Next create a new column that indicates if the data is for males or females. Simply type "Male" in the first 6 cells of C8, and "Female" in the next 6 cells.

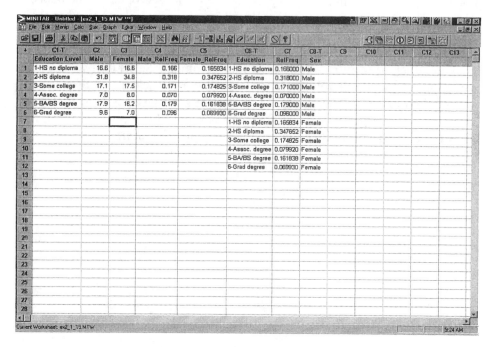

Now you are ready to create the bar graph.

To make the graph Click on **Graph → chart**. Select **RelFreq** for the Y-variable and **Education** for the X variable. Click beneath **For Each** and type in Group to tell Minitab that you want a different color rectangle for each group. Next click beneath **Group Variables** and select **Sex.**   This is telling Minitab that the variable Sex will separate our data into 2 groups. Click on **Annotation → Title** and change the title to an appropriate name. Click on **Options**, select **Cluster** and type in **Sex.** Click on **OK.** Minitab should still have all the tick mark settings, so click on **OK** again to view the bar graph.

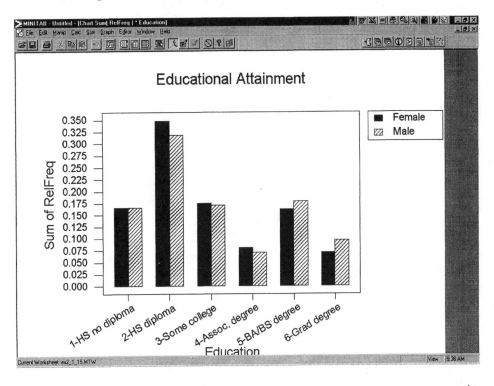

▶ Problem 19c,d,e (pg. 65)   Construct graphs
for 2000 Presidential election data

Open Minitab worksheet **2_1_19.**

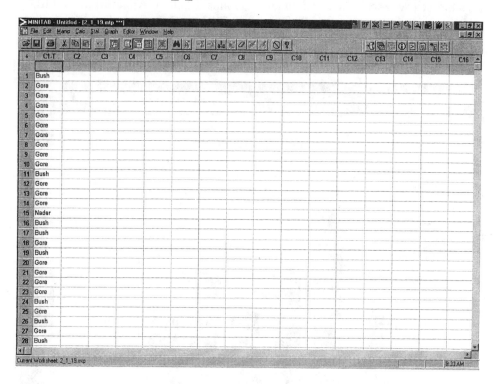

Click on **Graph → Chart.** Double-click on C1 to select it for the X-variable.
Add a title to the graph by clicking on **Annotation → title**. In Line 1, enter "Exit
Poll Results". Next add some axis labels by clicking on **Frame → axis**. Beneath
Label, enter "Candidate" in Line 1 for the X-axis and "Votes" in Line 2 for the
Y-axis. Click on **OK** twice and the histogram should appear.

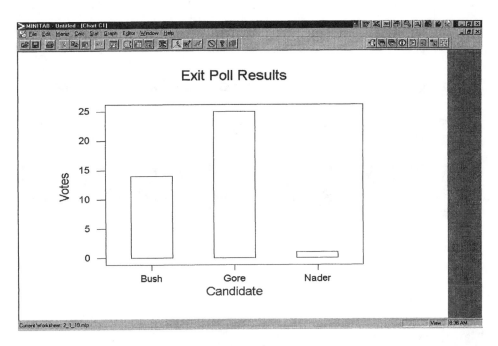

To create a Pie chart, click on **Graph → Pie chart.** On the screen that appears, select **Chart Data In** by clicking on the small circle to the left of it. Fill in C1 for the variable. Type in an appropriate **Title.** Click on **OK** to view the chart.

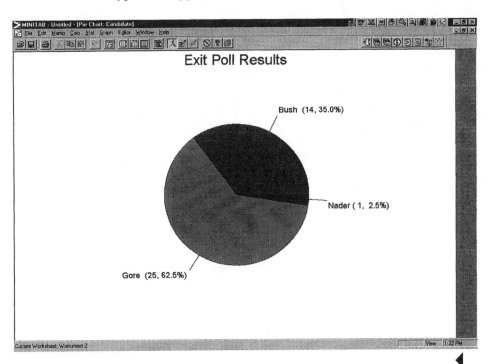

Section 2.2

▶ Example 2 (pg. 68): Construct a Histogram for Discrete data

To create this histogram, you must enter the 40 data points (Table 8 on page 68) into column 1 of the Minitab worksheet. Name the column "Arrivals".

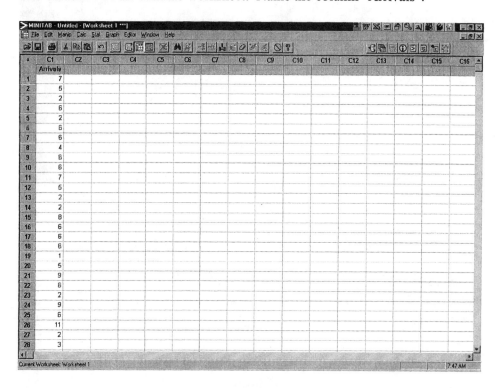

Now you are ready to make the histogram. Click on: **Graph → histogram**. First, double click on C1 in the large box at the left of the screen. "Arrivals" should now be filled in as Graph 1.

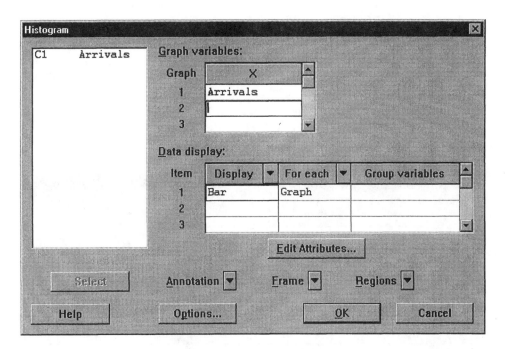

At this point, if you click on **OK**, MINITAB will draw a histogram using default settings. Your histogram will look like the one below.

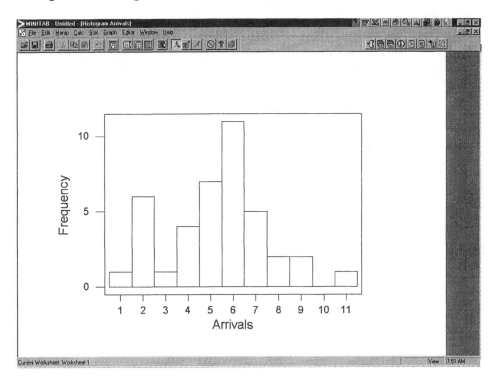

Notice that there is no title, and the numbering on the Y-axis is inadequate. We can instruct MINITAB to fix this, however. Close the Graph Window by clicking on the "X" in the upper right corner of the graph. Go back to the main Histogram screen. (Click on: **Graph → histogram**.) To change the numbering on the Y-axis, click on: **Frame → Tick**. Since the largest data value is 11, a possible numbering scheme could be from 1 to 11. To do this, in Line 2 (for the Y-axis), beneath **Positions**, type in **1:11/1.** This tells Minitab you want the numbering to go from 1 to 11 in steps of 1. Click on **OK**.

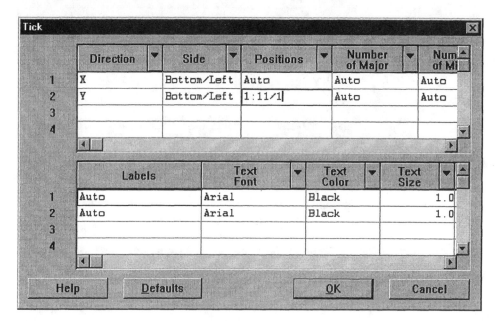

Next, to enter a title for the graph, click on **Annotation → Title.** Enter an appropriate title in Line 1.

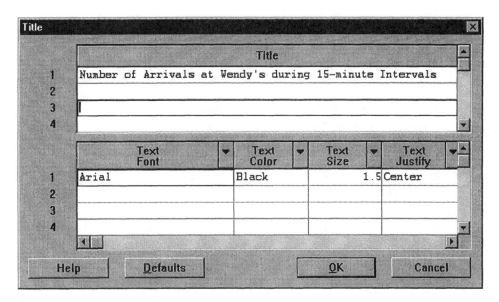

Click on **OK.** Minitab can draw frequency or relative frequency histograms. There are also other options available. To make a selection, click on **Options.**

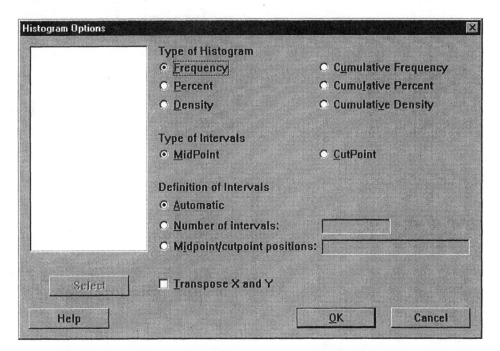

On the screen that appears, select **Frequency** as the **Type of Histogram** and **Midpoint** for **Type of Intervals**. Click on **OK** to go back to the main Histogram screen, and then click on **OK** again to view your Histogram.

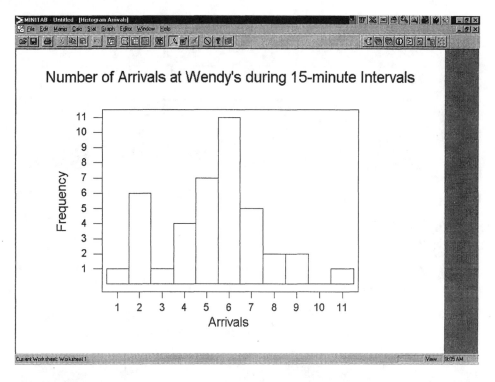

To print the graph, click on **File → Print Graph.** Next, click **OK** and the graph should print.

▶ Example 4 (pg. 72): Construct a Histogram for Continuous data

To create this histogram, open the Minitab worksheet **2_2_T12** .

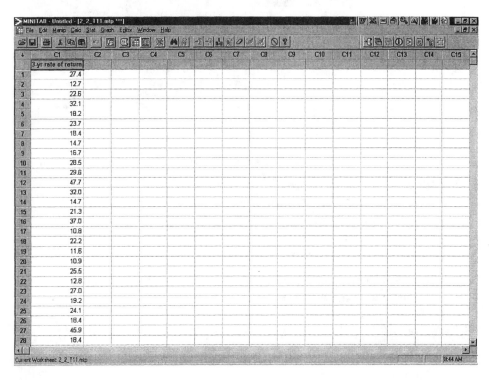

Now you are ready to make the histogram. Click on: **Graph → histogram**.
The following screen should appear. First, double click on C1 in the large box at
the left of the screen. "3-yr rate of return" should now be filled in as Graph 1.

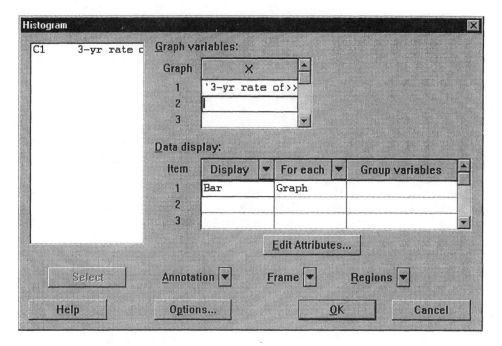

At this point, if you click on **OK**, MINITAB will draw a histogram using default settings. Your histogram will look like the one below.

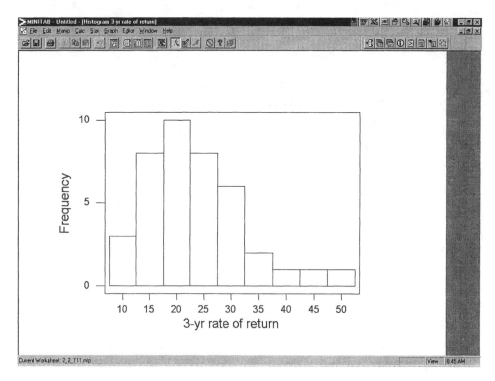

Notice that there is no title and the X-axis classes are not like the ones in the textbook, and tick marks are in the middle of the rectangles so it is difficult to tell what the classes are. We can instruct MINITAB to fix this, however. Close the Graph Window by clicking on the "X" in the upper right corner of the graph. Go back to the main Histogram screen. (Click on: **Graph** → **histogram**.) First, add an appropriate title. Click on: **Annotation** → **Title** and enter an appropriate title. Next, fix the numbering along the X-axis. Notice the textbook uses the numbers: 10, 15, 20, etc. The numbers are located at the beginning of each rectangle of the histogram. To do this, simply click on **Options**. On the screen that appears, select **Frequency** as the **Type of Histogram** and **Cutpoint** for **Type of Intervals**. Under **Definition of Intervals,** click on **Midpoint/cutpoint positions.** In the box to the right of it, type in: 10 : 50 / 5. This tells MINITAB that the first cutpoint is 10 and the last cutpoint is 50. The class width is 5, just as in the text.

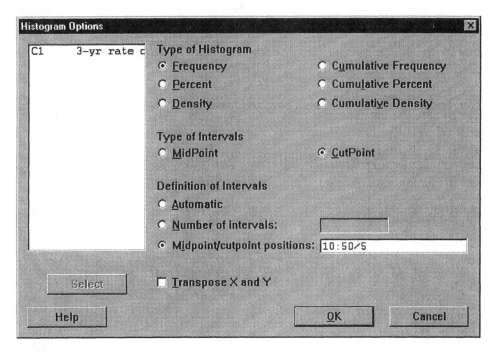

Click on **OK** to go back to the main Histogram screen. (**Note**: To create a relative frequency histogram, select **Percent** on the **Options** screen shown above.)

Next click on **Frame** → **Tick.** To set the tick marks along the Y-axis, move the cursor below **Positions** in Line 2 and enter "1 : 11 / 1" to tell Minitab that you want the tick marks to go from 1 to 11 in steps of 1.

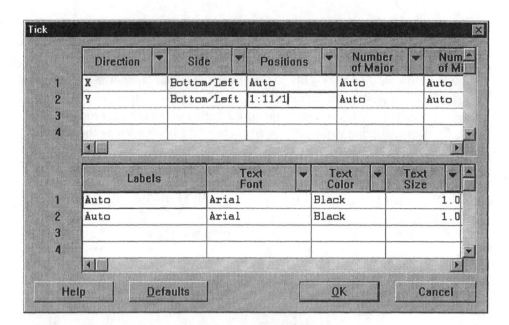

Click on **OK** to view the histogram.

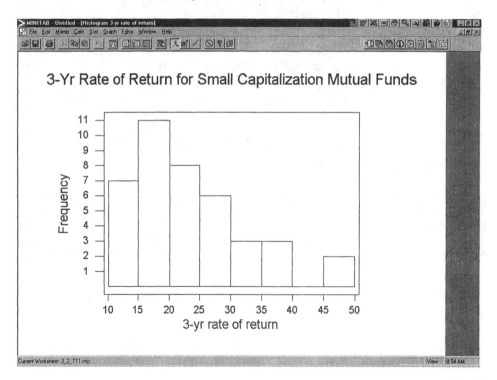

▶ Example 6 (pg. 74) Constructing a Stem-and-Leaf Plot

Open worksheet **2_2_T12.** To construct a Stem-and-leaf plot, click on **Graph** →
Stem-and-Leaf. On the screen that appears, select C1 as your **Variable** by
doubling clicking on C1.

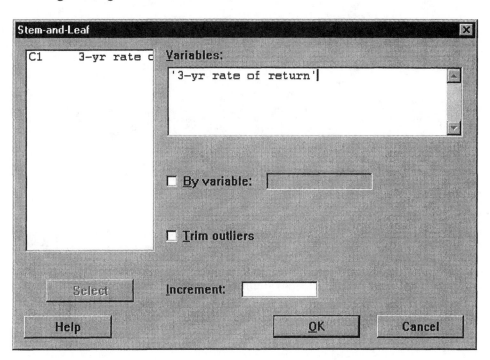

Click on **OK.**   The stem and leaf plot will be displayed in the Session Window.

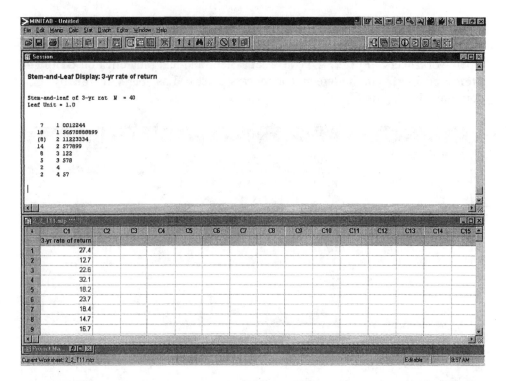

In this MINITAB display, the first column on the left is a counter. This column counts the number of data points starting from the smallest value (at the top of the plot) down to the median. It also counts from the largest data value (at the bottom of the plot) up to the median. Notice that there are seven data points in the first row of the stem and leaf plot so the counter is "7". Row 2 has 11 data points so the counter increases to "18" (7+11=18). The row that contains the median has the number "8" in parentheses. This number counts the number of data points that are in the row that contains the median. There are no data points in row 7, so the counter on the left remains at "2".

The second column in the display is the **Stem**. In this example, the Stem values range from 1 to 4. Notice that this display contains two rows for each of the values. These are called **split-stems**. For each stem value, the first row contains all data points with leaf values from 0 to 4 and the second row contains all data points with leaf values from 5 to 9. Notice that MINITAB constructs an *ordered* stem and leaf.

The leaf values are shown to the right of the stem. The leaf values may be the actual data points or they may be the rounded data points. To find the actual values of the data points in the display, use the "Leaf Unit=" statement at the top of the display. The "Leaf Unit" gives you the place value of the leaves. In this stem and leaf plot, the first data point has a stem value of 1 and a leaf value of 0.

Since the "Leaf Unit=1.0", the leaf value of 0 is the "ones" place and the stem value of 1 is the "tens" places. Thus the data point is 10.

◀

▶ Problem 19c,d (pg. 80): Tensile Strength

To create this histogram, open the Minitab worksheet **2_2_19.**

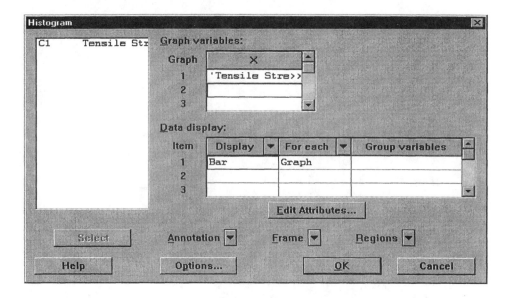

Click on: **Graph → histogram**. First, double click on C1 in the large box at the left of the screen. "Tensile Strength" should now be filled in as Graph 1.

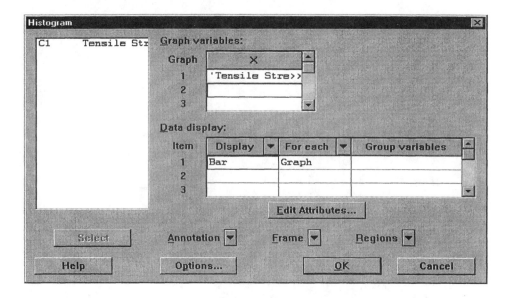

At this point, if you click on **OK**, MINITAB will draw a histogram using default settings. Since you need to add an appropriate title and have specific class limits to set, you do not want the default histogram. First, add an appropriate title. Click on: **Annotation** → **Title** and enter an appropriate title. Next, fix the numbering along the X-axis. The instructions for this problem say to set the first class limit to 160 and to have a class width of 10. To do this, simply click on **Options**. On the screen that appears, select **Frequency** as the **Type of Histogram** and **Cutpoint** for **Type of Intervals**. Under **Definition of Intervals,** click on **Midpoint/cutpoint positions.** In the box to the right of it, type in: 160 : 250 / 10. This tells MINITAB that the first cutpoint is 160 and the last cutpoint is 250. The class width is 10 as instructed. Click on **OK** to go back to the main Histogram screen, and then click on **OK** again to view your frequency Histogram.

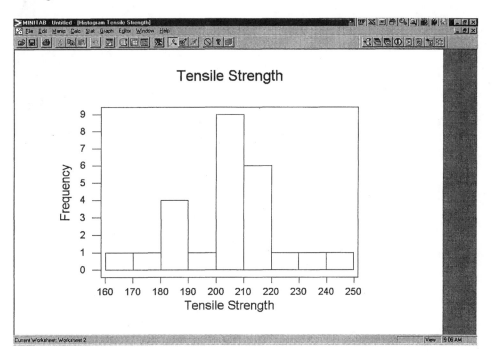

To create a relative frequency histogram, select **Percent** on the **Options** screen. All other settings remain the same. Click on **OK** twice to view the relative frequency histogram.

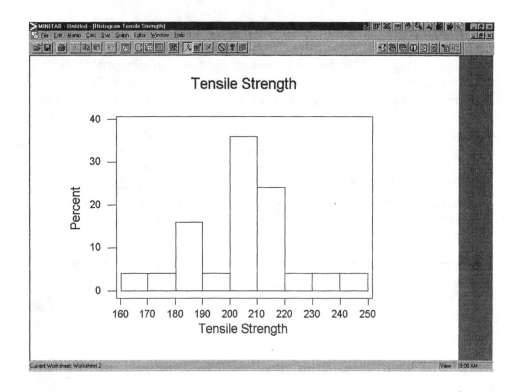

> ▶ **Problem 21 (pg. 81):** Serum HDL

To create this histogram, open the Minitab worksheet **2_2_21.** Click on **Graph → histogram**. First, double click on C1 in the large box at the left of the screen. "Serum HDL" should now be filled in as Graph 1. At this point, if you click on **OK**, MINITAB will draw a histogram using default settings. Since you need to add an appropriate title and have specific class limits to set, you do not want the default histogram. First, add an appropriate title. Click on: **Annotation → Title** and enter an appropriate title. Next, fix the numbering along the X-axis. The instructions for this problem say to set the first class limit to 20 and to have a class width of 10. To do this, simply click on **Options**. On the screen that appears, select **Frequency** as the **Type of Histogram** and **Cutpoint** for **Type of Intervals**. Under **Definition of Intervals,** click on **Midpoint/cutpoint positions.** In the box to the right of it, type in: 20 : 80 / 10. This tells MINITAB that the first cutpoint is 20 and the last cutpoint is 80. The class width is 10 as instructed. Click on **OK** to go back to the main Histogram screen, and then click on **OK** again to view your frequency Histogram. To add more tick marks to the Y-axis than are used with the default setting, click on **Frame → Tick.** For the Y-axis, enter 0:14 / 2 beneath **Positions** in Line 2.

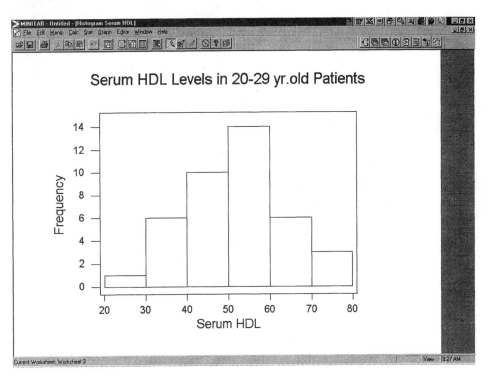

To create a relative frequency histogram, select **Percent** on the **Options** screen. Be sure to change the tick marks (**Frame → Tick**) so that they represent percent and not frequency. In the picture below, tick mark **Position** is set at 0:35/5 for the Y-axis.

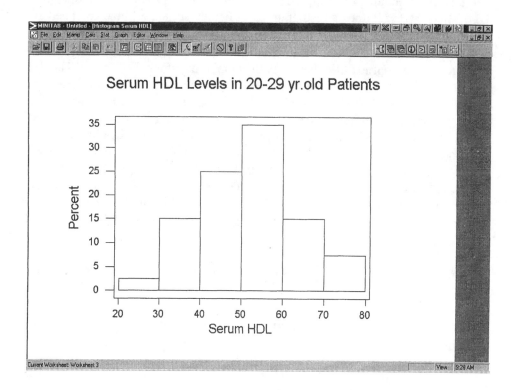

Section 2.3

▶ Polygon (pg. 85) Constructing Frequency Polygons

A frequency polygon is created the same way as a histogram in MINITAB.
Open the worksheet **2_2_T12.** The Rate of Return data should be in column 1.
Click on **Graph →histogram.** First, double click on C1 in the large box at the
left of the screen. "3-yr Rate of Return" should now be filled in as Graph 1.
Beneath **Display**, select **Connect.** Then in Line 2, select **Symbol** for each
Graph. This tells Minitab to draw a line graph with a symbol at each value
instead of rectangles for the histogram.

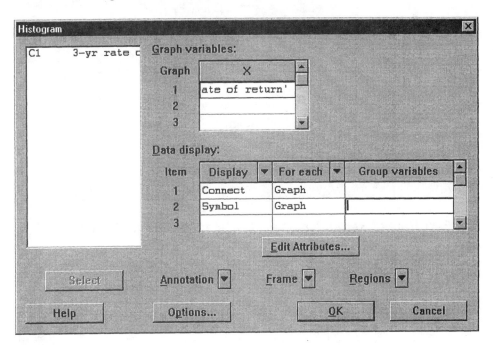

Next, add an appropriate title. Click on: **Annotation → Title** and enter an
appropriate title. Next, fix the numbering along the X-axis. This time we want to
use the midpoints of each class. To do this, simply click on **Options**. On the
screen that appears, select **Frequency** as the **Type of Histogram** and **Midpoint**
for **Type of Intervals**. Under **Definition of Intervals,** click on
Midpoint/cutpoint positions. In the box to the right of it, type in:
12.45 : 47.45 / 5. This tells MINITAB that the first midpoint is 12.45 and the last
midpoint is 47.45. The class width is 5.

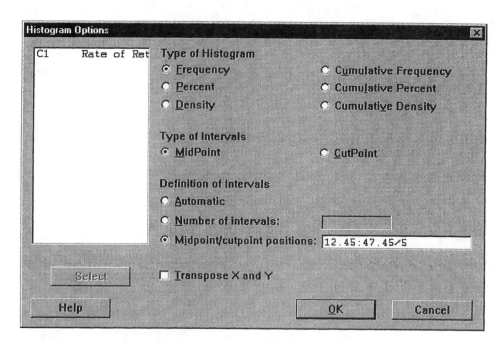

Click on **OK** to go back to the main Histogram screen, and then click on **OK** again to view your frequency Polygon.

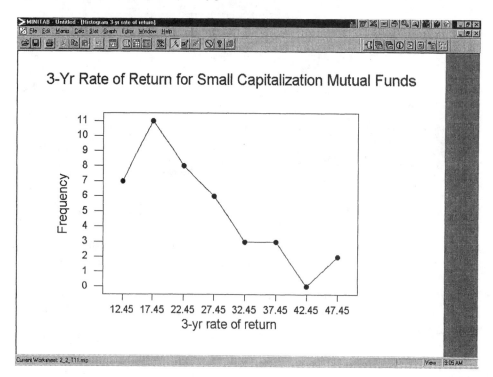

▶ Ogives (pg. 87) Constructing an Ogive

In this example, you must enter the data into the Data Window. Minitab does not have an automatic ogive function, but can plot the data for you after you enter the upper class limits and the cumulative relative frequencies. Begin with a clean worksheet. From Table 18 on page 87 of the text, enter the upper class limits into C1 and the cumulative relative frequencies into C2. Label each column appropriately as shown below.

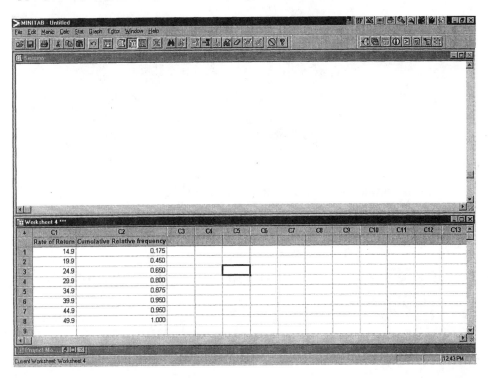

To plot the data, click on **Graph → Plot**. In the screen that appears, select C2 for the **Y-variable** and C1 for the **X-variable**. Beneath **Display**, select **Connect** in Line 1. Then in Line 2, select **Symbol.** Be sure that you have also selected **For each** Graph. By choosing both **Symbol** and **Connect**, Minitab will now put a dot at each data point on the graph.

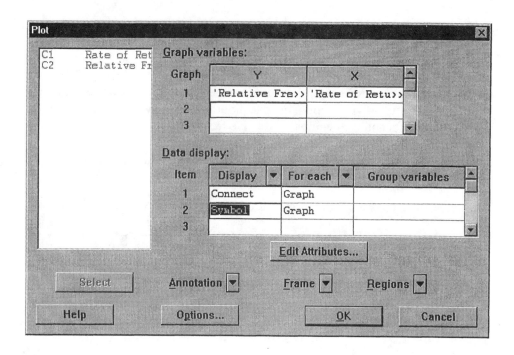

Click on **Annotation → Title** and enter an appropriate title. Next, tell Minitab that you want the tick marks on the X-axis to be the values that you entered into C1. Click on **Frame → Tick** and enter the X-axis tick mark **Positions** in Line 1 as 14.9: 49.9/ 5.

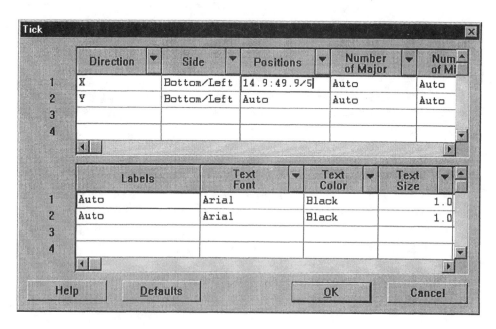

Click on **OK** twice to view the ogive.

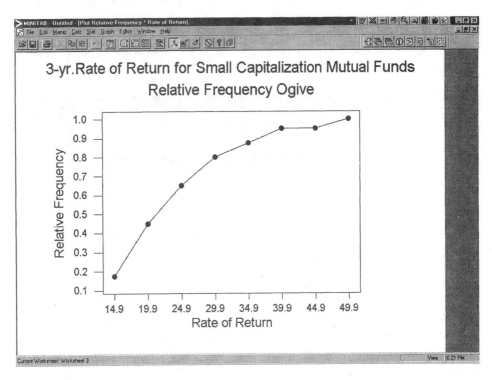

▶ Example 1 (pg. 88) Constructing Time Series Plots

Open worksheet **2_3_T19.** Click on **Graph→ Time Series Plot.** Select
C2(Closing Price) as the **Y variable.** Select a **Time Scale** by clicking on
Calendar and selecting **Month.** Under **Display,** select **Connect** and then also
select **Symbol** in Line 2. This tells Minitab to put a "dot" at each time point in
our graph.

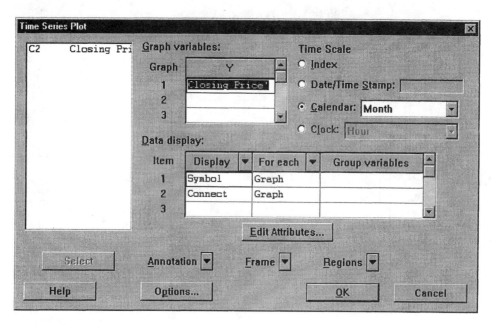

Click on **Annotation → Title** and enter an appropriate title for the plot. Next,
click on **Frame → Tick.** To make the dates easier to read, you can place them at
an angle. For row 1 under **Labels,** type in **Date** to tell Minitab to use the dates in
C1 for the tick labels. Next, scroll to the right and click on the down arrow to the
right of **Text Angle** and select '90'. You must also click on the down arrow to
the right of **Horizontal Placement** and select 'To the left of', and also click on
the down arrow to the right of **Vertical Placement** and select 'Centered On'.

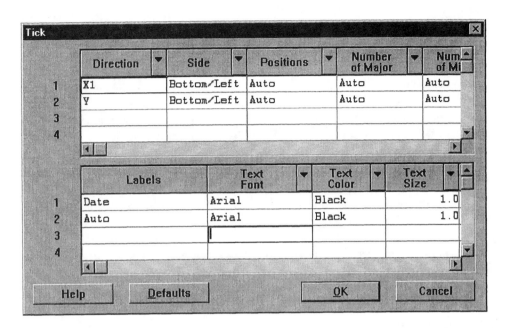

Click on **OK** twice, and then view the plot.

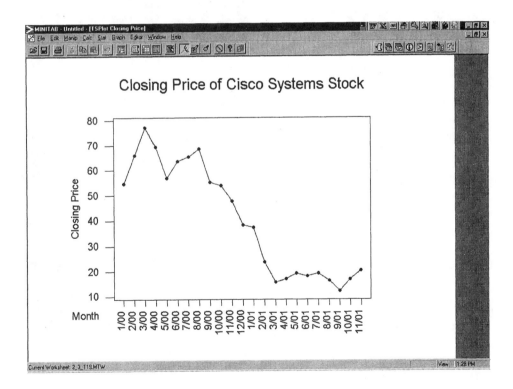

▶ Problem 9c-e (pg. 90) Graphs of Serum HDL

Open worksheet **2_2_21.** The Serum Cholesterol data should be in column 1.
Click on **Graph →histogram.** First, double click on C1 in the large box at the
left of the screen. "Serum HDL Cholesterol" should now be filled in as Graph 1.
Beneath **Display,** select **Connect** in Line 1 and **Symbol** in Line 2. Be sure to
select **For each** Graph. This tells Minitab to draw a line graph instead of
rectangles for the histogram. Next, add an appropriate title. Click on: **Annotation**
→ **Title** and enter an appropriate title. Fix the numbering along the X-axis
because for a polygon you should use the midpoints of each class. One
possibility is to have classes be 31-35, 36-40, etc. The class midpoints are 33,
38, etc. To use these, simply click on **Options**. On the screen that appears, select
Frequency as the **Type of Histogram** and **Midpoint** for **Type of Intervals.**
Under **Definition of Intervals,** click on **Midpoint/cutpoint positions.** In the
box to the right of it, type in: 33 : 73 / 5. This tells MINITAB that the first
midpoint is 33 and the last midpoint is 73. The class width is 5. Click on OK
twice to view the polygon.

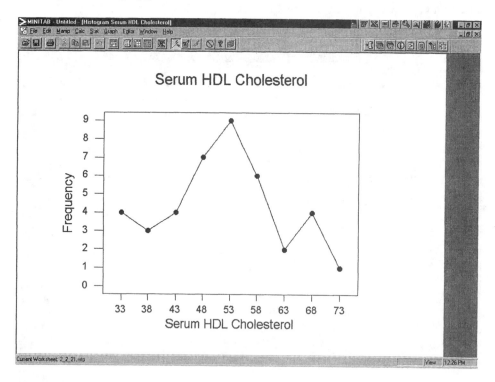

Part d and e of this problem are to draw ogives for this data. You will have to
enter the frequency distribution into the worksheet, as well as the cumulative

frequencies, relative frequencies, cumulative relative frequencies, and upper class limits. Using the classes above, the worksheet will look like the one below.

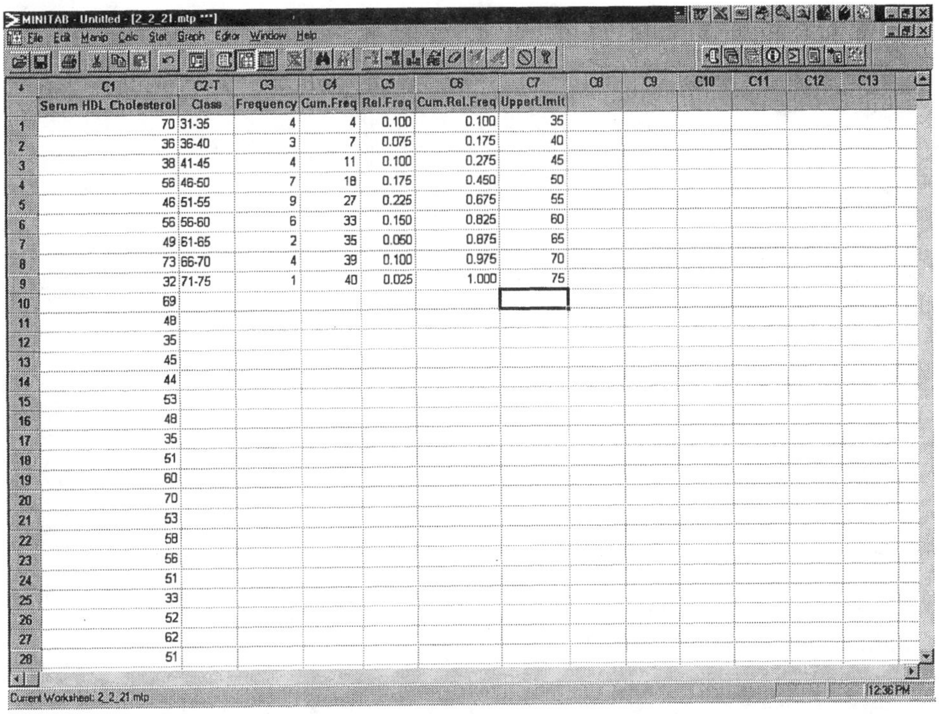

MINITAB - Untitled - [2_2_21.mtp ***]

↓	C1 Serum HDL Cholesterol	C2-T Class	C3 Frequency	C4 Cum.Freq	C5 Rel.Freq	C6 Cum.Rel.Freq	C7 UpperLimit
1	70	31-35	4	4	0.100	0.100	35
2	36	36-40	3	7	0.075	0.175	40
3	38	41-45	4	11	0.100	0.275	45
4	56	46-50	7	18	0.175	0.450	50
5	46	51-55	9	27	0.225	0.675	55
6	56	56-60	6	33	0.150	0.825	60
7	49	61-65	2	35	0.050	0.875	65
8	73	66-70	4	39	0.100	0.975	70
9	32	71-75	1	40	0.025	1.000	75
10	69						
11	48						
12	35						
13	45						
14	44						
15	53						
16	48						
17	35						
18	51						
19	60						
20	70						
21	53						
22	58						
23	56						
24	51						
25	33						
26	52						
27	62						
28	51						

Current Worksheet: 2_2_21.mtp

To draw an ogive, you will be using the upper class limits. Notice that they are entered in C7. To plot the cumulative frequencies, click on **Graph → Plot**. In the screen that appears, select "cum.freq" for the **Y-variable** and "UpperLimit" for the **X-variable**. Beneath **Display**, select **Connect** in Line 1. Then in Line 2, select **Symbol.** Be sure that you have also selected **For each** Graph. By choosing both **Symbol** and **Connect**, Minitab will now put a dot at each data point on the graph. Click on **Annotation → Title** and enter an appropriate title. Next, tell Minitab that you want the tick marks on the X-axis to be the values that you entered into C1. Click on **Frame → Tick** and enter the X-axis tick mark **Positions** in Line 1 as 35:75/ 5. Click on **Frame → Axis** and enter the X-axis **Label** as Serum HDL because the default label is column name and "UpperLimit" is not a good name for the axis in the graph. Click on **OK** twice to view the ogive.

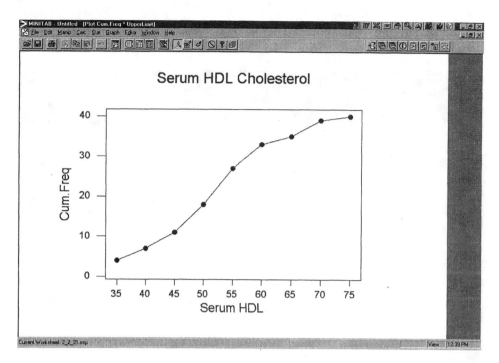

To create a relative frequency ogive, repeat all the steps above but select the column "cum.rel.freq" for the Y-axis variable.

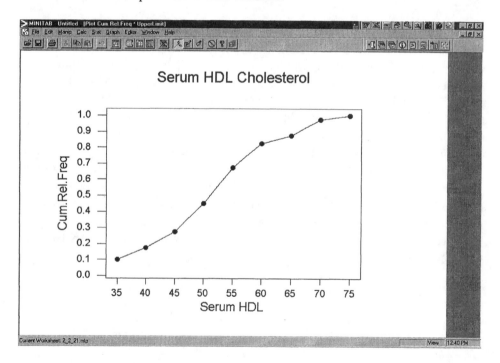

▶ Problem 15 (pg. 91) Rates of Returns of Stocks

Enter the frequency distributions in a worksheet as shown below. Notice that all columns that will be needed for polygons and ogives are there.

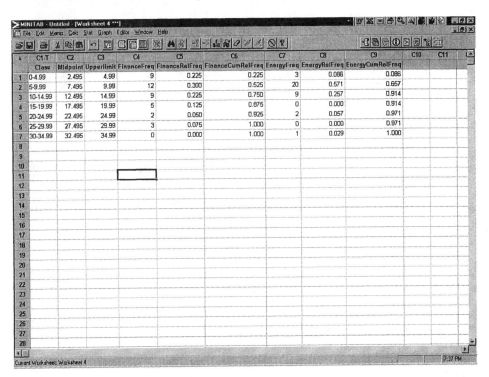

To construct the polygons, you will be using the class midpoints. Notice that they are entered in C2. Since the data is summarized in a frequency distribution, you should use the plot function instead of the histogram function. To plot the relative frequencies, click on **Graph → Plot**. In the screen that appears, select "FinanceRelFreq" for the **Y-variable** and "Midpoint" for the **X-variable**. For Graph 2, select "EnergyRelFreq" for the **Y-variable** and "Midpoint" for the **X-variable**. Beneath **Display**, select **Connect** in Line 1. Then in Line 2, select **Symbol.** Be sure that you have also selected **For each** Graph. By choosing both **Symbol** and **Connect**, Minitab will now put a dot at each data point on the graph.

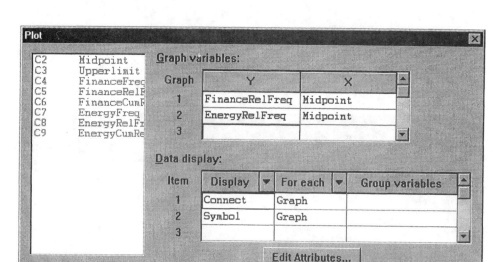

Click on **Annotation** → **Title** and enter an appropriate title. Next, tell Minitab that you want the tick marks on the X-axis to be the values that you entered into C1. Click on **Frame** → **Tick** and enter the X-axis tick mark **Positions** in Line 1 as 2.495:32.495/ 5. Click on **Frame** → **Axis** and enter the X-axis **Label** as "Rate of Return" because the default label is column name and "Midpoint" is not a good name for the axis in the graph. Also, enter "Relative Frequency" as the Y-axis label. Finally, to tell Minitab to graph both stocks on the same page, click on **Frame** → **Multiple Graphs**. Select **Overlay graphs on the same page.**

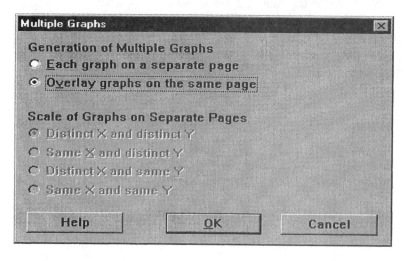

Click on **OK** twice to view the polygon.

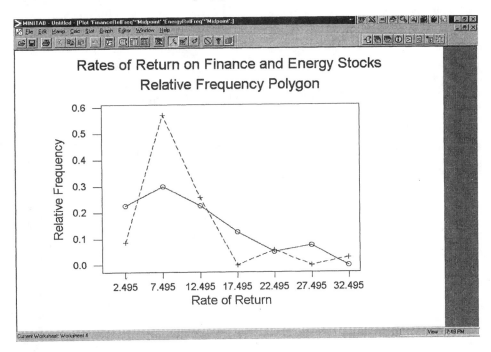

To make a relative frequency ogive, click on **Graph** → **Plot** and simply change the Y-axis variables to "FinanceCumRelFreq" for Graph 1 and "EnergyCumRelFreq" for Graph 2. Also, change the X-axis variables to "UpperLimit".

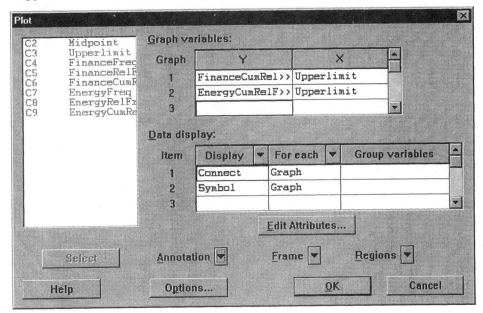

Click on **Annotation → Title** and enter an appropriate title. Next, tell Minitab that you want the tick marks on the X-axis to be the upper class limits. Click on **Frame → Tick** and enter the X-axis tick mark **Positions** in Line 1 as 4.99:34.99/ 5. Click on **Frame → Axis** and enter the X-axis **Label** as "Rate of Return" because the default label is column name and "UpperLimit" is not a good name for the axis in the graph. Also, enter "Cumulative Relative Frequency" as the Y-axis label. Finally, to tell Minitab to graph both stocks on the same page, click on **Frame → Multiple Graphs**. Select **Overlay graphs on the same page.**

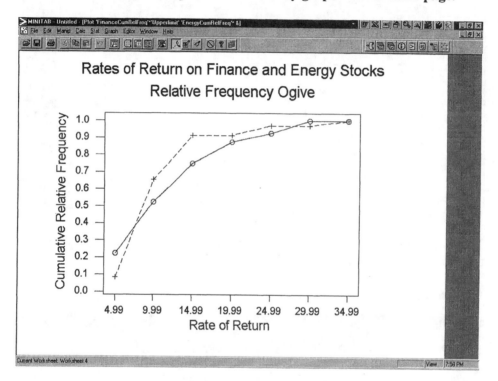

Numerically Summarizing Data

Section 3.1

▶ Example 1 (pg. 113) Population mean and Sample mean

Finding the mean and standard deviation of a dataset is very easy using
MINITAB. Open the Minitab worksheet **3_1_Ex1.** Column 2 contains the
number of homeruns hit by the 14 teams. To find the mean of this data, click on
Stat → Basic Statistics → Display Descriptive Statistics. You should see the
input screen below.

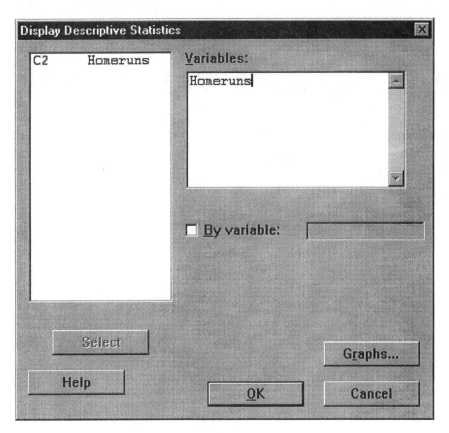

Double click on C2 to select the homerun data that is entered in C2. Click on **OK** and the descriptive statistics should appear in the Session Window.

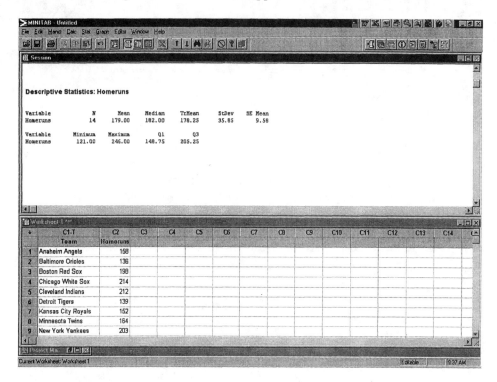

Notice that MINITAB displays several descriptive statistics: sample size, mean, median, trimmed mean, standard deviation, standard error of the mean, minimum value, maximum value, and the first and third quartiles. So, the population mean number of homeruns is 179.

Now, take a random sample of 5 teams. Click on **Calc → Random Data → Sample from Columns.** You want to **Sample 5 rows from column C2** and **Store in C3.**

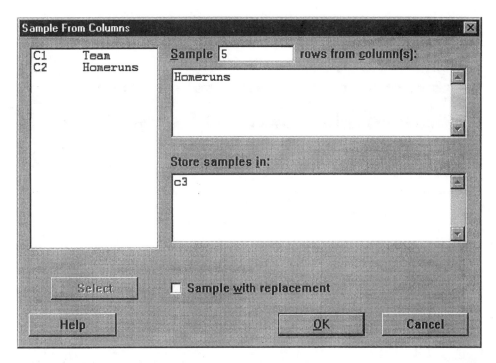

Click on **OK** to see the sample data. Since this is a *random* sample, your data will not look exactly like the data below.

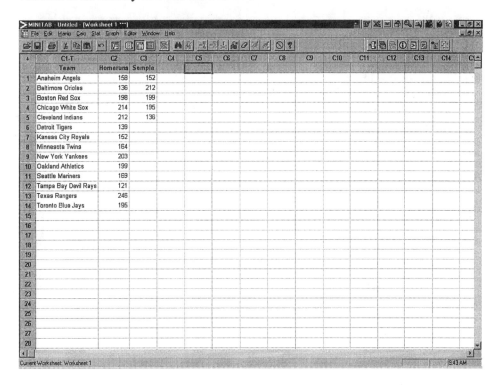

To find the sample mean of this data, click on **Stat→ Basic Statistics →
Display Descriptive Statistics.** Select C3 this time, click on **OK** and view the
sample mean number of homeruns.

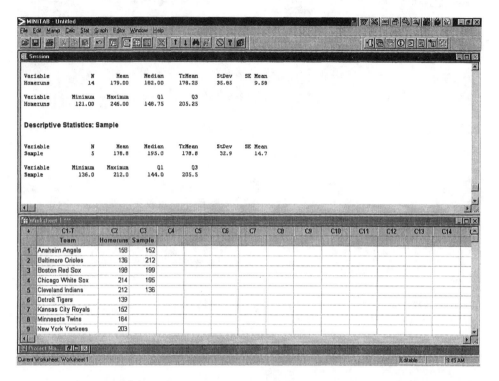

As you can see, the sample mean is 178.8 and is very close to the population
mean in this example.

▶ Example 2 & 3 (pg. 116-117) Finding the median

Finding the median of a dataset is very easy using MINITAB. (Look at the
Minitab output in Example 1 to see that the median number of homeruns is 182.)
To find the median of Example 3, enter the song lengths into C1 of a Minitab
worksheet. Click on **Stat → Basic Statistics → Display Descriptive Statistics.**
Select C1 and, click on **OK** to see the summary statistics.

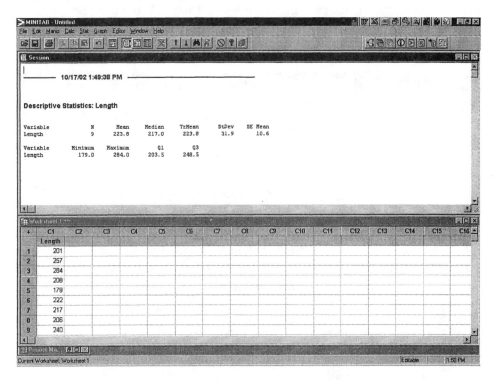

As you can see, the median length is 217.

▶ Example 4 (pg. 118) Finding the mode

The mode is NOT produced automatically by the above procedure, however, it is quite simple to have MINITAB tally up the data values for you, and then you can select the one with the highest count. Enter the data for this example into C1 of a Minitab worksheet. Click on **Stat → Tables → Tally**. On the input screen, double-click on C1 to select it. Also, click on **Counts** to have MINITAB count up the frequencies for you.

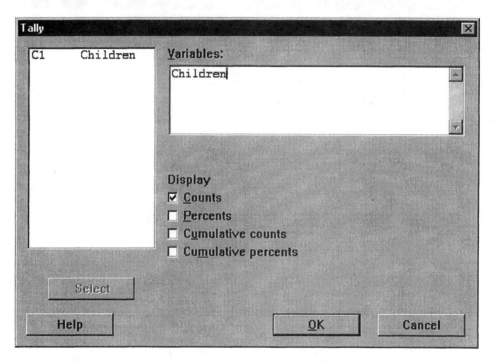

When you click on **OK**, a frequency table will appear in the Session Window.

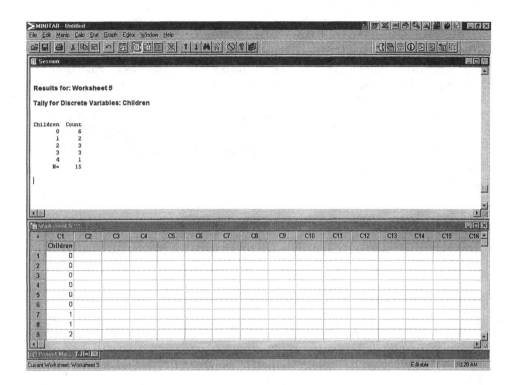

Notice that 0 has a count of 6. This means that 6 members of the math department have 0 children. Since 6 is the highest count, 0 is the mode. To print the Session Window with the frequency table in it, click anywhere up in the Session Window to be sure that it is the active window. Next click on **File → Print Session Window**.

▶ Example 8 (pg. 121) Mean, median and shape of Birth weights

Enter the birth weights into C1. Click on **Stat**→ **Basic Statistics** → **Display Descriptive Statistics.** Select C1 and, click on **OK** to see the summary statistics.

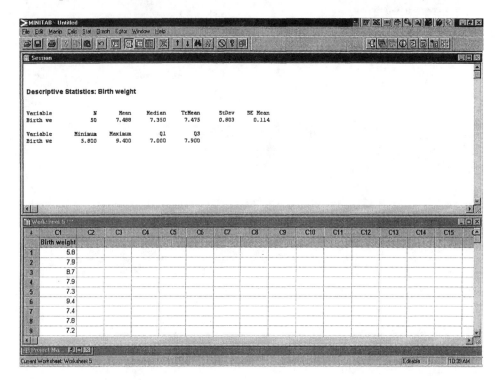

A histogram is a good way to see the shape of the data. We will let Minitab help us by using its default settings. Click on **Graph**→ **Histogram.** Select C1 as the **Graph** variable. Click on **OK** to view the histogram.

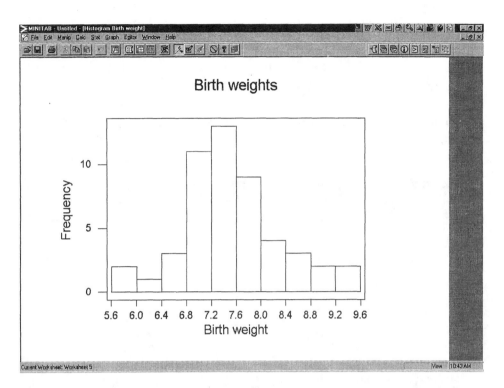

Notice that the cutpoints chosen automatically by Minitab are not exactly the
same as those in the textbook. This is not important since the shape of the
distribution is of interest here. Notice that this histogram is fairly symmetric and
bell-shaped.

▶ Problem 11 (pg. 125) Pulse Rates

Enter the pulse rates into C1 of the Minitab worksheet. To take 2 random
samples of size 3, click on **Calc → Random Data → Sample from Columns.**
You want to **Sample 3 rows from column C1** and **Store in C2.** Repeat and this
time **Store in C3.** Click on **Stat → Basic Statistics → Display Descriptive
Statistics.** Select C1-C3 and click on **OK** to see the summary statistics.

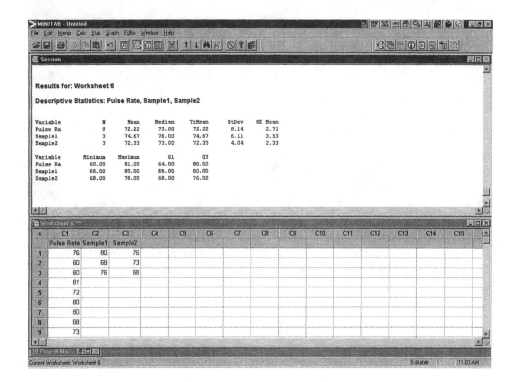

▶ Problem 13 (pg. 125) Waiting for a Table

Open worksheet **3_1_13**. The number of customers waiting should be in C1.
Click on **Stat → Basic Statistics → Display Descriptive Statistics.** Select C1
and click on **OK** to see the summary statistics.

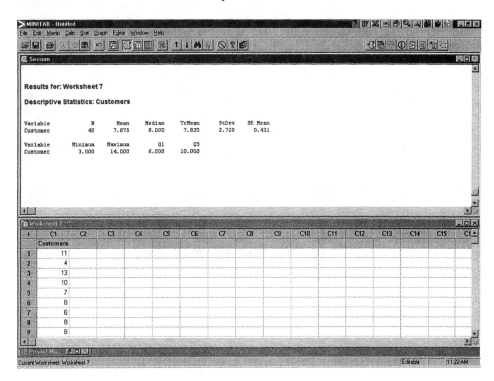

The mean is 7.875 and the median is 8.

To create the histogram, click on **Graph → Histogram.** Select C1 as the **Graph**
variable. Click on **Frame → Tick** and enter X-axis tick mark **Positions** as
3:14/1. Click on **Annotation → Title** and add an appropriate title. Click on **OK**
twice to view the histogram.

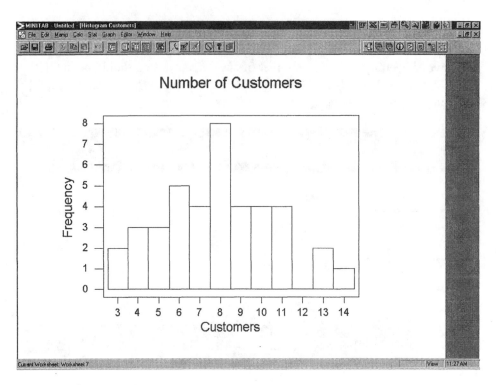

The shape of the histogram is fairly symmetric.

Section 3.2

▶ Example 6 (pg. 138) Comparing the Variance and Standard
                         Deviation of Two Datasets

Open Minitab worksheet **3_2_Ex1**. Click on **Stat → Basic Statistics → Display
Descriptive Statistics.** Select both C1 and C2, and click on **OK** to see the
summary statistics.

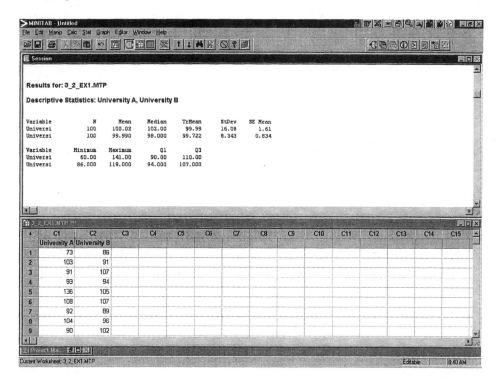

▶ Problem 31 (pg. 147) Understanding the Standard Deviation

Enter the 5 data values into C1 of a Minitab worksheet. Click on **Stat→ Basic
Statistics → Display Descriptive Statistics.** Select C1 and click on **OK** to see
the summary statistics. Notice the standard deviation is 11.63.

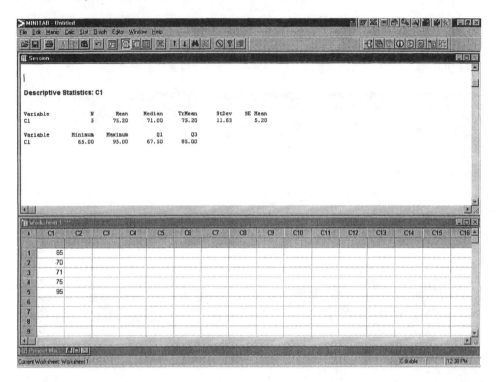

Now add 4 points to data value. Click on **Calc→ Calculator. Store Result In**
C2, and enter the **Expression** C1 + 4. Click on OK and column 2 should contain
the data values. Now, click on **Stat → Basic Statistics → Display Descriptive
Statistics.** Select C2 and click on **OK** to see the summary statistics. Notice that
the standard deviation is still 11.63.

Descriptive Statistics: C2

Variable	N	Mean	Median	TrMean	StDev
SE Mean					
C2	5	79.20	75.00	79.20	11.63
5.20					

Variable	Minimum	Maximum	Q1	Q3
C2	69.00	99.00	71.50	89.00

Now multiply each data value by 2. Click on **Calc** → **Calculator**. **Store Result In** C3, and enter the **Expression** C1 * 2. Click on OK and column 3 should contain the data values. Now, click on **Stat** → **Basic Statistics** → **Display Descriptive Statistics.** Select C3 and click on **OK** to see the summary statistics. Notice that the standard deviation is 23.3, which is 11.63 * 2 when rounded.

Descriptive Statistics: C3

Variable SE Mean	N	Mean	Median	TrMean	StDev
C3 10.4	5	150.4	142.0	150.4	23.3

Variable	Minimum	Maximum	Q1	Q3
C3	130.0	190.0	135.0	170.0

◀

Section 3.3

▶ Example 1,3 (pg. 151, 153) Computing the Mean and Standard
Deviation from a Frequency Distribution

Enter the lower class limits into C1 and the upper class limits into C2 of a
Minitab worksheet. To calculate the midpoints, click on **Calc→ Calculator**.
Store Results In C3 and enter the **Expression** C1+(C2-C1)/2. Click on **OK** to
see the midpoints in C3. Now enter the frequencies into C4.

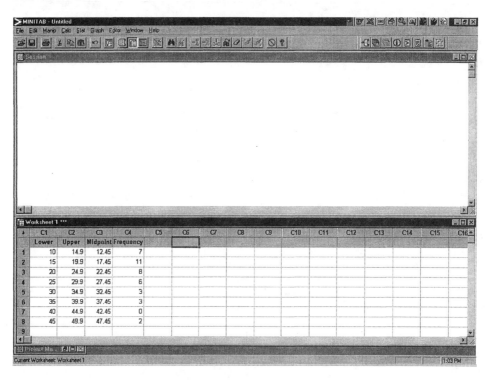

To calculate the mean of the grouped data, click on **Calc → Calculator**. **Store
Results In** C5 and enter the **Expression** Sum(C3*C4)/Sum(C4). Click on **OK** to
see the mean in C5. Copy the mean into each cell of C5. Now subtract the mean
from each midpoint. Click on **Calc → Calculator**. **Store Results In** C6 and
enter the **Expression C3-C5**. Click on **OK** to see the differences in C6. Now
square the differences. Click on **Calc → Calculator**. **Store Results In** C7 and
enter the **Expression C6*C6**. Click on **OK** to see the squared differences in C7.
Finally, multiply the squared differences by the frequencies. Click on **Calc→
Calculator**. **Store Results In** C8 and enter the **Expression C7*C4**. Click on
OK.

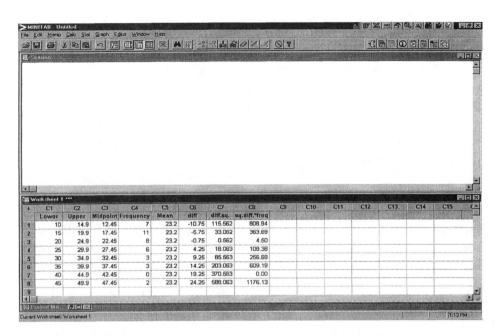

To calculate the *population* variance, click on **Calc → Calculator. Store Results In** C9 and enter the **Expression** Sum(C8)/sum(C4). Click on **OK.** To calculate the *sample* variance, click on **Calc → Calculator. Store Results In** C10 and enter the **Expression** Sum(C8)/(sum(C4)-1). Click on **OK.** To calculate the standard deviations, repeat the above calculations taking the square root of each expression: Sqrt(Sum(C8)/sum(C4)) and Sqrt(Sum(C8)/(sum(C4)-1).

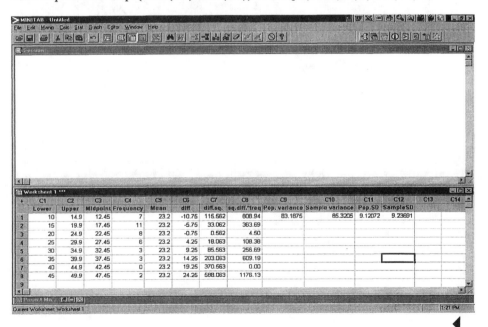

▶ Problem 3 (pg. 155) Meteorology

Enter the lower class limits into C1 and the upper class limits into C2 of a
Minitab worksheet. To calculate the midpoints, click on **Calc→ Calculator**.
Store Results In C3 and enter the **Expression** C1+(C2-C1)/2. Click on **OK** to
see the midpoints in C3. Now enter the frequencies into C4. To calculate the
mean of the grouped data, click on **Calc → Calculator**. **Store Results In** C5
and enter the **Expression** Sum(C3*C4)/Sum(C4). Click on **OK** to see the mean
in C5. Copy the mean into each cell of C5 (use cut & paste). Now subtract the
mean from each midpoint. Click on **Calc → Calculator**. **Store Results In** C6
and enter the **Expression C3-C5**. Click on **OK** to see the differences in C6.
Now square the differences. Click on **Calc → Calculator**. **Store Results In** C7
and enter the **Expression C6*C6**. Click on **OK** to see the squared differences in
C7. Finally, multiply the squared differences by the frequencies. Click on **Calc
→ Calculator**. **Store Results In** C8 and enter the **Expression C7*C4**. Click on
OK. To calculate the *population* variance, click on **Calc → Calculator**. **Store
Results In** C9 and enter the **Expression** Sum(C8)/sum(C4). Click on **OK.** To
calculate the *sample* variance, click on **Calc→ Calculator**. **Store Results In**
C10 and enter the **Expression** Sum(C8)/(sum(C4)-1). Click on **OK.** To calculate
the standard deviations, repeat the above calculations taking the square root of
each expression: Sqrt(Sum(C8)/sum(C4)) and Sqrt(Sum(C8)/(sum(C4)-1)).

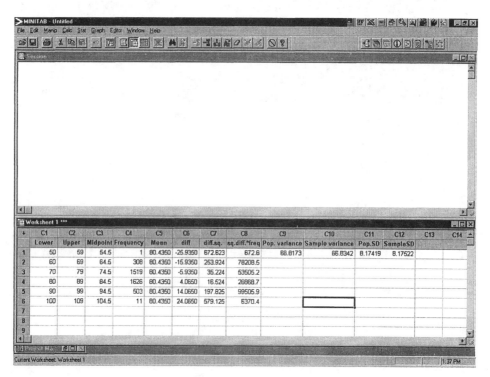

To make a graph of the data, click on **Graph → Chart**. Select the Frequencies as your **Y-variable** and the Midpoints as your **X-variables**. Since you only want to see the shape of the data, use the Minitab default settings for everything else. Click on **OK** to view the graph.

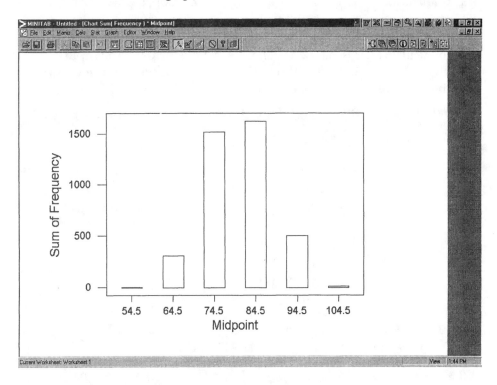

Section 3.4

▶ Exploration (pg. 159) Computing the Z-scores

Open Minitab worksheet **3_1_Ex1**. Column 2 contains the number of homeruns hit. To calculate the Z-scores, click on **Calc → Standardize**. The **Input column** is C2, and you should **Store results in** C3. Click on **Subtract mean and divide by std. dev.,** then click on **OK**.

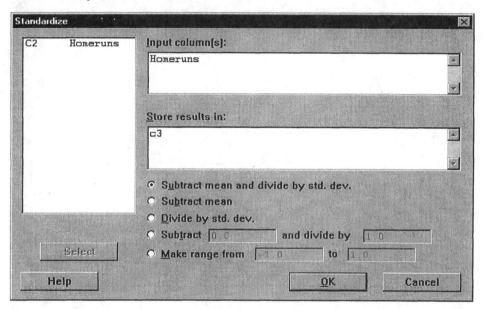

The Z-scores should be in C3.

	Team	Homeruns	Z-scores
1	Anaheim Angels	158	-0.58584
2	Baltimore Orioles	136	-1.19958
3	Boston Red Sox	198	0.53005
4	Chicago White Sox	214	0.97640
5	Cleveland Indians	212	0.92061
6	Detroit Tigers	139	-1.11589
7	Kansas City Royals	152	-0.75323
8	Minnesota Twins	164	-0.41846
9	New York Yankees	203	0.66953
10	Oakland Athletics	199	0.55795
11	Seattle Mariners	169	-0.27897
12	Tampa Bay Devil Rays	121	-1.61804
13	Texas Rangers	246	1.86912
14	Toronto Blue Jays	195	0.44636

To calculate the mean and standard deviation of the Z-scores, click on **Stat** →
Basic Statistics → **Display Descriptive Statistics.** Select C3 and click on **OK**
to see the summary statistics.

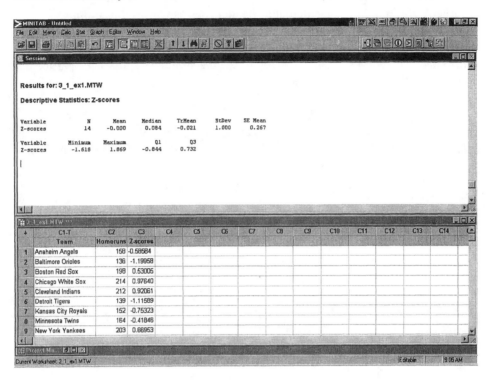

Notice that the mean is 0 and the standard deviation is 1.

► Example 4 (pg. 162) Computing the Quartiles

Open Minitab worksheet **3_4_Ex2**. Column 1 contains the earnings of the top 130 PGA golfers. Minitab calculates the quartiles as part of the summary statistics and uses a slightly different formula for the calculations because it is more accurate. Click on **Stat → Basic Statistics → Display Descriptive Statistics.** Select C1 and click on **OK** to see the summary statistics. Notice that the median is the second quartile.

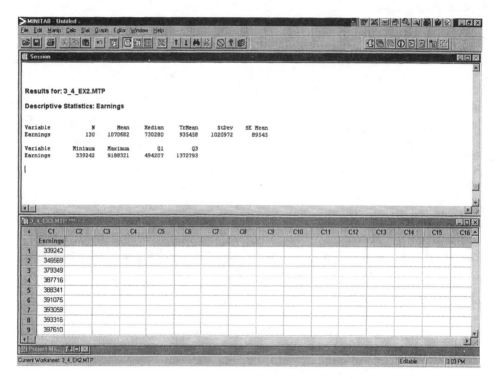

▶ Problem 9   (pg. 165)   April Showers

Open Minitab worksheet **3_4_9**. The rainfall is in Column 1 of the Minitab
worksheet. To calculate the Z-scores, click on **Calc → Standardize**. The **Input
column** is C1, and you should **Store results in** C2. Click on **Subtract mean
and divide by std. dev.,** then click on **OK**. Now it is easy to find the Z-score for
any data point. To calculate the quartiles of the rainfall data, click on **Stat→
Basic Statistics → Display Descriptive Statistics**. Select C1 and click on **OK**
to see the summary statistics.

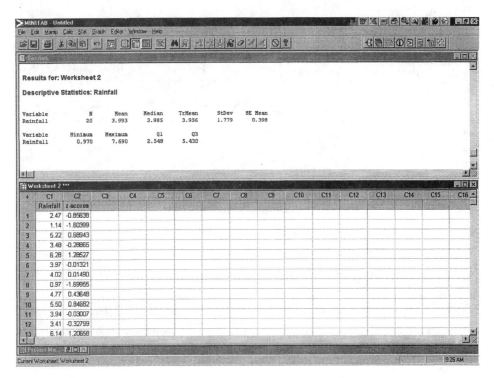

Section 3.5

▶ Example 2 (pg. 170) Constructing a Boxplot

Open Minitab worksheet **2_2_T12**. The rate of return data is in C1. Minitab produces the 5-number summary as part of the summary statistics. Click on **Stat → Basic Statistics → Display Descriptive Statistics.** Select C1 and click on **OK** to see the summary statistics. To draw a boxplot, click on **Graph→ Boxplot.** Select C1 for the **Y**-variable and leave the **X**-variable blank.

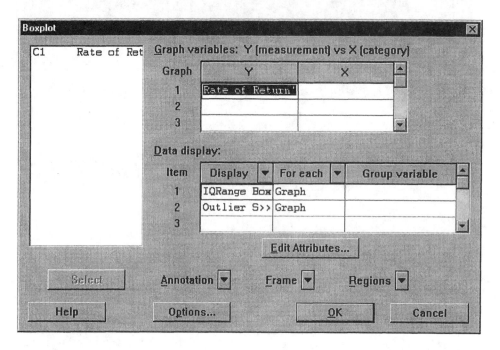

Click on **Annotation → Title** and enter an appropriate title. If you click on OK now, you will see a boxplot drawn with the default settings.

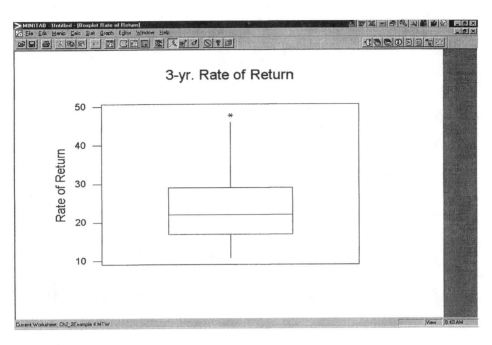

Notice that this boxplot is vertical instead of horizontal, as in the textbook. To fix this, close the graph and go back to the main boxplot screen. Click on **Options** and select **Transpose X and Y.**

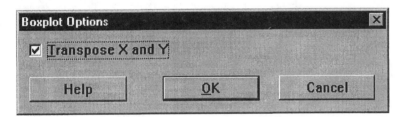

Click on **OK**. It will be easier to read the boxplot if you set the tick mark positions. Click on **Frame → Tick.** Set the positions for the Y-variable to 10:50/2. This tells Minitab to put a tick mark from 10 to 50 in steps of 2.

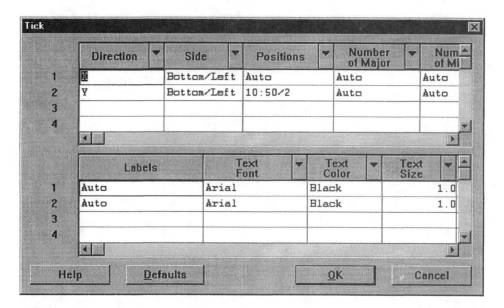

Click on **OK** twice to view the boxplot.

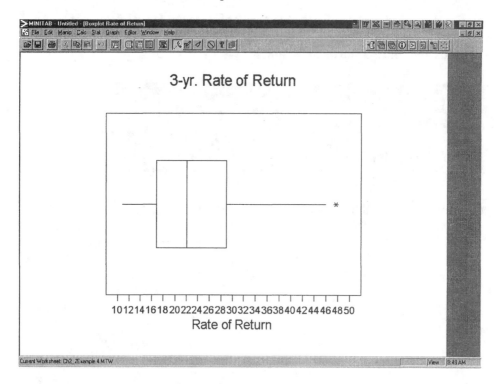

Notice that there is one outlier at approximately 48. Look at the data values in column 1 to find the exact value of the outlier. It is the largest data point, 47.7.

▶ Example 3 (pg. 172) Comparisons using Boxplots

Enter the data into a Minitab datasheet. Put the Flight data in C1 and the Control data in C2. To draw the boxplots, click on **Graph** → **Boxplot**. Select C1 for the **Y**-variable and leave the **X**-variable blank. Then in Line 2, select C2 for the **Y**-variable and leave the **X**-variable blank. Click on **Annotation** → **Title** and enter an appropriate title. Click on **Options** and select **Transpose X and Y.** It will be easier to read the boxplot if you set the tick mark positions. Click on **Frame**→ **Tick.** Set the positions for the Y-variable to 6:10/0.5. This tells Minitab to put a tick mark from 6 to 10 in steps of 0.5. You should also label the horizontal axis to show that the units of measurement are millimeters. Click on **Frame**→ **Axis** and in the lower half of the screen, enter "Millimeters" in Line 2 as the label for the Y variable. Finally, to graph both boxplots on the same graph, click on **Frame** → **Multiple Graphs.** Select **Overlay graphs on the same page**. Click on **OK** to view the boxplots.

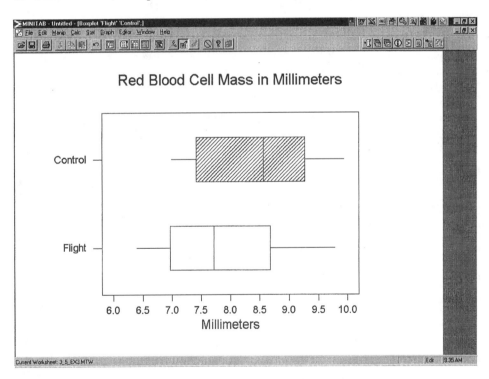

▶ Problem 3 (pg. 173) Age at Inauguration

Open Minitab worksheet **3_5_3**. The Age data is in C1. To find the 5-number summary, click on **Stat** → **Basic Statistics** → **Display Descriptive Statistics**. Select C1 and click on **OK** to see the summary statistics.

Descriptive Statistics: Age

Variable	N	Mean	Median	TrMean	StDev
SE Mean					
Age	43	54.814	55.000	54.744	6.235
0.951					

Variable	Minimum	Maximum	Q1	Q3
Age	42.000	69.000	51.000	58.000

To draw the boxplot, click on **Graph** → **Boxplot**. Select C1 for the **Y**-variable and leave the **X**-variable blank. Click on **Annotation** → **Title** and enter an appropriate title. Click on **Options** and select **Transpose X and Y**. It will be easier to read the boxplot if you set the tick mark positions. Click on **Frame** → **Tick.** Set the positions for the Y-variable to 40:70/2. This tells Minitab to put a tick mark from age 40 to age 70 in steps of 2 years. Click on **OK** to view the boxplots.

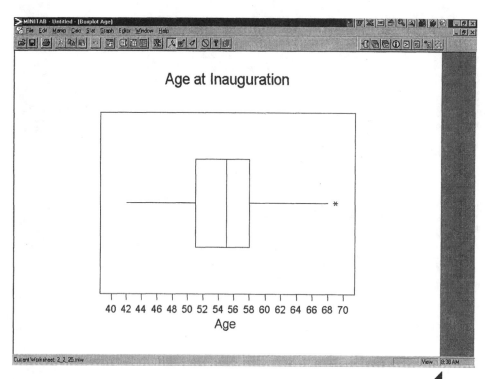

Describing the Relation between Two Variables

CHAPTER

4

Section 4.1

▶ Example 1 (pg. 193) Drawing a Scatter Diagram

Open Minitab worksheet **4_1_Ex1**. The per capita GDP should be in C2, and the
life expectancy should be in C3. Notice that per capita GDP is the x-variable and
life expectancy is the y-variable. To plot the data, click on **Graph → Plot.** On
the input screen, enter C3 for the **Y variable** and C2 for the **X variable.**

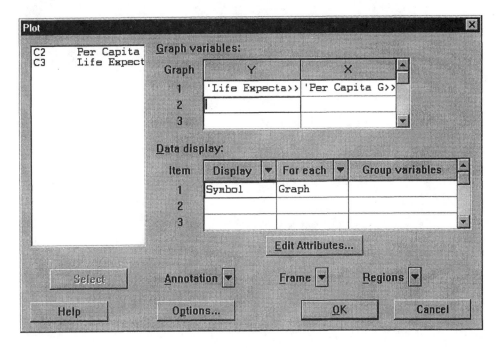

Next, click on **Annotation → Title.** Enter an appropriate title. Click on **OK**
twice to view the scatter plot that is created using Minitab default settings. If you
need to change settings, the **Plot** function has the same drop down menus as
other graphs that you have used.

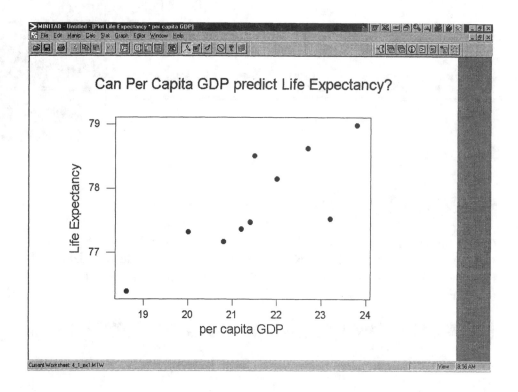

▶ Example 2 (pg. 197) Finding the Correlation Coefficient

Open Minitab worksheet **4_1_Ex1**. The per capita GDP should be in C2, and the life expectancy should be in C3. Notice that per capita GDP is the x-variable and life expectancy is the y-variable. To find the correlation coefficient, click on **Stat → Basics Statistics → Correlation.** On the input screen, select both C2 and C3 for **Variables**, by double-clicking on each one.

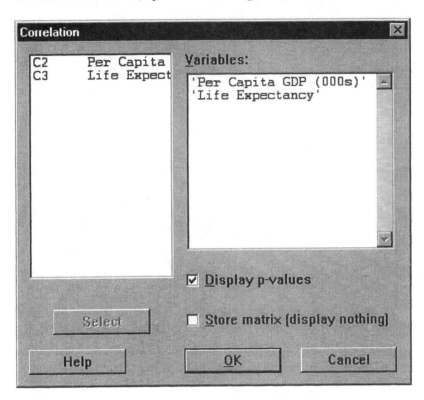

Click on **OK** and the Correlation Coefficient will be displayed in the Session Window.

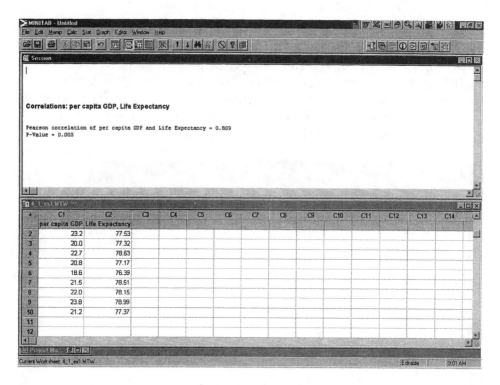

As you can see, the correlation coefficient is .809.

> ▶ Problem 11 (pg. 200) Height vs. Head Circumference

Open Minitab worksheet **4_1_11**. The height should be in C1, and head circumference should be in C2. Notice that "Height" is the x-variable and "Head Circumference" is the y-variable. To plot the data, click on **Graph → Plot.** On the input screen, enter C2 for the **Y variable** and C1 for the **X variable.** Next, click on **Annotation → Title.** Enter an appropriate title. Click on **OK** to view the scatter plot.

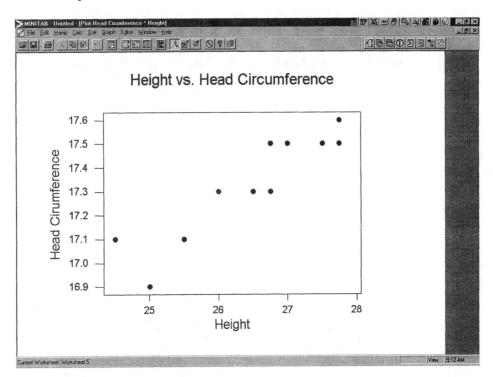

Now, to find the correlation coefficient, click on **Stat → Basics Statistics → Correlation.** On the input screen, select both C1 and C2 for **Variables**, by double-clicking on each one. Click on **OK** and the following output should be in the Session Window.

Correlations: Height, Head Cirumference

```
Pearson correlation of Height and Head Cirumference = 0.911
P-Value = 0.000
```

So, as you can see, the correlation coefficient is 0.911.

Section 4.2

▶ Example 2 (pg. 210) Finding a Regression Equation

Open Minitab worksheet **4_1_Ex1**. The per capita GDP should be in C2, and life expectancy should be in C3. Notice that "Per Capita GDP" is the x-variable and "Life Expectancy" is the y-variable. To find the least squares regression equation, click on **Stat → Regression → Regression.** Enter C3 for the **Response** variable, and C2 as the **Predictor.**

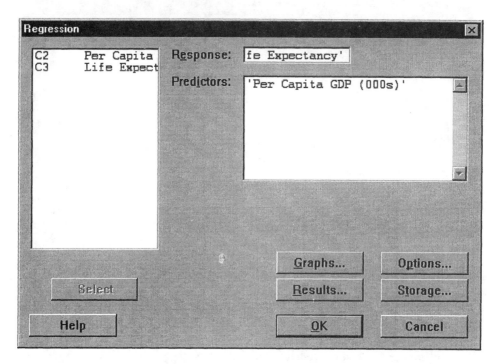

Click on **Results.** Select **Regression equation, table of coefficients, s, R-squared, and basic analysis of variance.**

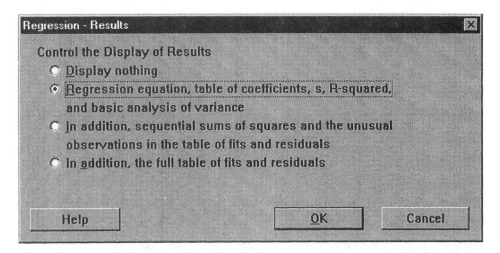

Next, click on **Storage** and select **Residuals.** Minitab will calculate the residuals for each data point and store them in an empty column.

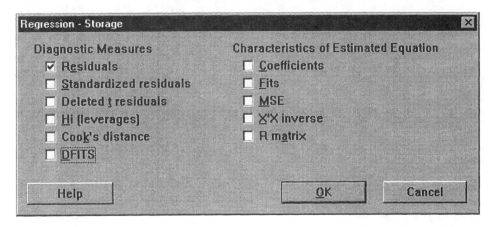

To tell Mintab to predict the life expectancy of a resident in Italy where the per capita GDP is \$21.5, click on **Options** and enter 21.5 for **Prediction intervals for new observations.** Be sure to select **Fits.**

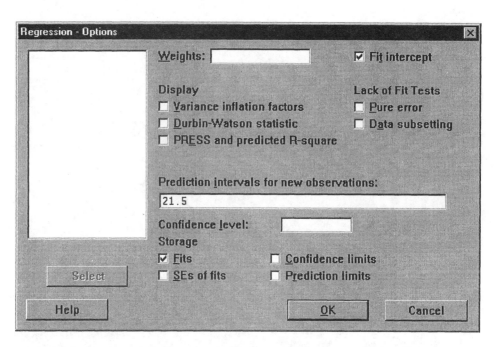

Click on **OK** to view the output in the Session Window and the Data Window.

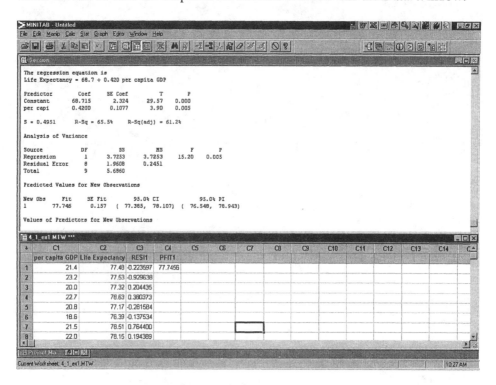

Notice that the regression equation is Life Expectancy = 68.7 + .42 * Per capita
GDP.   Also, in the data window there are now 2 extra columns. The column

labeled **RESI1** contains the residuals. Italy is the data in row 7 with a residual of .7644. The column labeled **PFIT1** contains the predicted value for Italy, 77.7456.

◀

▶ Problem 11 (pg. 217)   Gestation Period vs. Life Expectancy

Open worksheet **4_2_11**. Gestation period is in C2 and Life Expectancy is in C3.
First plot the data. Click on **Graph→ Plot.** On the input screen, enter C3 for
the **Y variable** and C2 for the **X variable.** Click on **OK.**

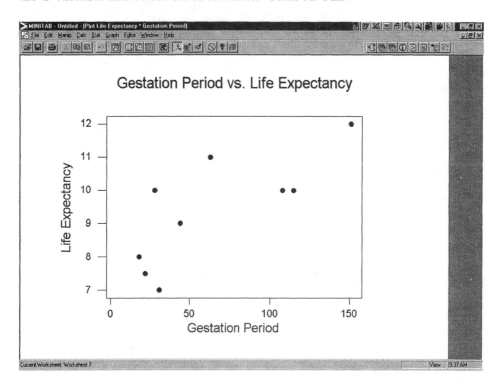

To find the regression equation, click on **Stat→ Regression → Regression.**
Enter C2 for the **Response** variable, and C1 as the **Predictor.** Click on **Results.**
Select **Regression equation, table of coefficients, s, R-squared, and basic
analysis of variance.** Next, click on **Storage** and select **Residuals.** Minitab will
calculate the residuals for each data point and store them in an empty column. To
tell Mintab to predict the life expectancy of a new species with a gestation
period of 95 days, click on **Options** and enter 95 for **Prediction intervals for
new observations.** Be sure to select **Fits.** Click on **OK.**

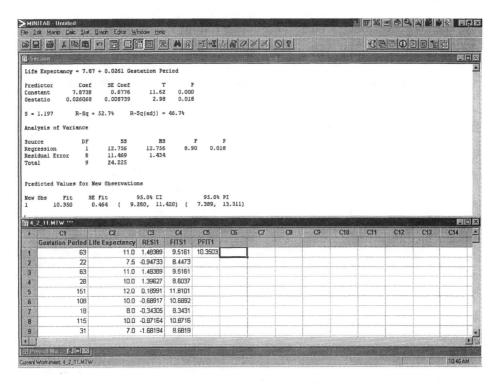

The regression equation is Life Expectancy = 7.87 + .261 * Gestation Period. The predicted life expectancy for the new species is 10.35 years. From the data window, the parakeet has a gestation period of 18 days, and a predicted life expectancy of 8.3431 years. Repeat the steps above to find the predicted life expectancy of the guinea pig, which has a gestation period of 68 days.

Section 4.3

▶ Example 1 (pg. 223)   Finding the Coefficient of Determination

Open worksheet **4_1_EX1**. Per Capita GDP is in C2 and Life Expectancy is in
C3. The coefficient of determination is part of the regression output. To find the
regression equation, click on **Stat → Regression → Regression.** Enter C3 for
the **Response** variable, and C2 as the **Predictor.** Click on **Results.** Select
**Regression equation, table of coefficients, s, R-squared, and basic analysis of
variance.** Click on **OK** twice.

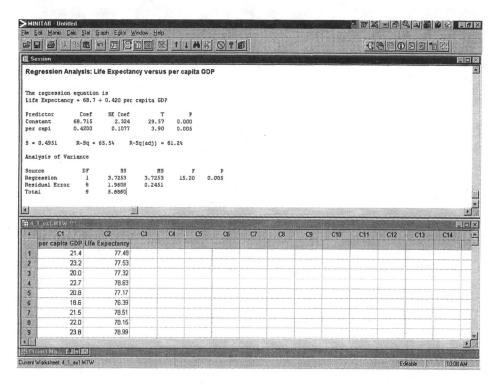

Notice that the coefficient of determination is R-Sq = 65.5%.

▶ Example 2 (pg. 226)   Is a Linear Model Appropriate?

Enter the two columns of data (found on page 226 of the textbook) into the
MINITAB Data Window. Enter the years into C1 and name it Year. Enter the
prices into C2 and name it Closing Price. To find the regression equation, click
on **Stat → Regression → Regression.** Enter C2 for the **Response** variable, and
C1 as the **Predictor.** Click on **OK.** Click on **Results.** If you would like to see
the other regression output, then select **Regression equation, table of
coefficients, s, R-squared, and basic analysis of variance.**   Finally, click on
Graphs and beneath **Residuals versus the variables:** enter C1.

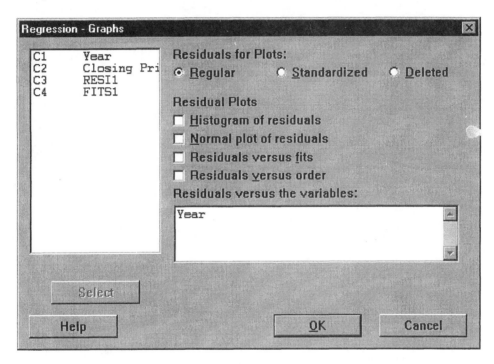

Click on **OK** twice and view the graph.

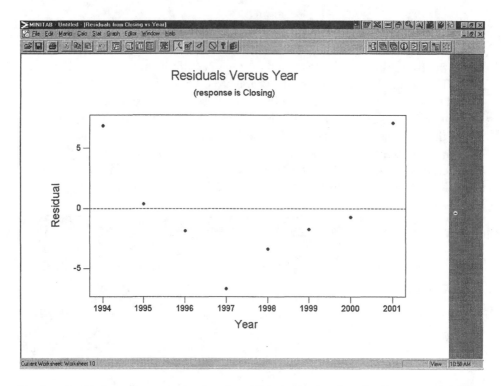

Notice the U-shaped pattern in the plot. This indicates that the linear model is not appropriate.

▶ Example 5 (pg. 228) Graphical Residual Analyses

Open Minitab worksheet **4_1_Ex1**. The per capita GDP should be in C2, and life expectancy should be in C3. Notice that "Per Capita GDP" is the x-variable and "Life Expectancy" is the y-variable. To find the least squares regression equation, click on **Stat → Regression → Regression.** Enter C3 for the **Response** variable, and C2 as the **Predictor.** Next, click on **Storage** and select **Residuals.** Minitab will calculate the residuals for each data point and store them in an empty column. You will use this column to create the boxplot of the residuals. Click on **Results.** If you would like to see the other regression output, then select **Regression equation, table of coefficients, s, R-squared, and basic analysis of variance.** Finally, click on **Graphs** and enter C2 beneath **Residuals versus the variables**. Click on **OK** to view the residual plot.

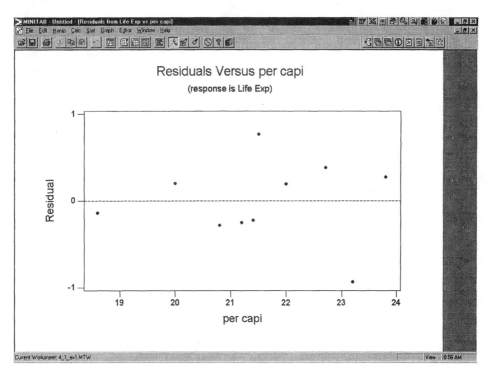

Notice that the residual for Belgium (per capita GDP is close to 23) looks like a possible outlier. To check this, create a boxplot of the residuals. The residuals should now be C4, labeled RESI1. Click on **Graph → Boxplot** and select C4 for the **Y**-variable. Click on **Options** and select **Transpose X and Y.** You may want to add an appropriate title (**Annotation → Title**). Click on **OK** to view the boxplot of the residuals.

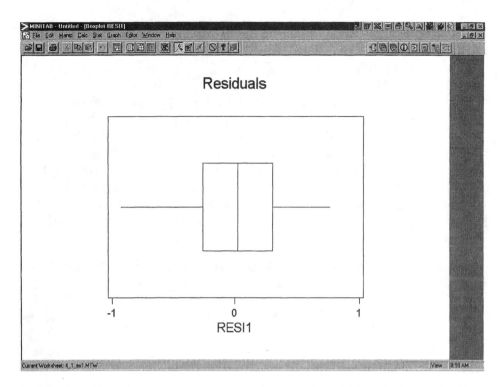

Notice that there are no outliers shown on the boxplot. Although the residual corresponding to Belgium looked rather large, it is not identified as an outlier by the boxplot.

▶ Example 6 (pg. 229) Identifying Influential Observations

Open Minitab worksheet **4_1_Ex1**. The per capita GDP should be in C2, and life expectancy should be in C3. Add the data for Greece to the bottom of the worksheet. Type 13.9 into C2 and 78.44 into C3. Notice that "Per Capita GDP" is the x-variable and "Life Expectancy" is the y-variable. To find the least squares regression equation, click on **Stat** → **Regression** → **Regression.** Enter C3 for the **Response** variable, and C2 as the **Predictor.** Next, click on **Storage** and select **Residuals.** Minitab will calculate the residuals for each data point and store them in an empty column. You will use this column to create the boxplot of the residuals. Click on **Results.** If you would like to see the other regression output, then select **Regression equation, table of coefficients, s, R-squared, and basic analysis of variance.**   Finally, click on **Graphs** and enter C2 beneath **Residuals versus the variables**. Click on **OK** to view the residual plot.

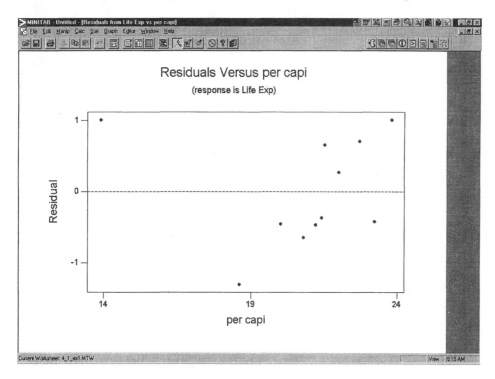

Notice that the residual corresponding to Greece (located above 14) is very different. Look at the output from the regression analysis.

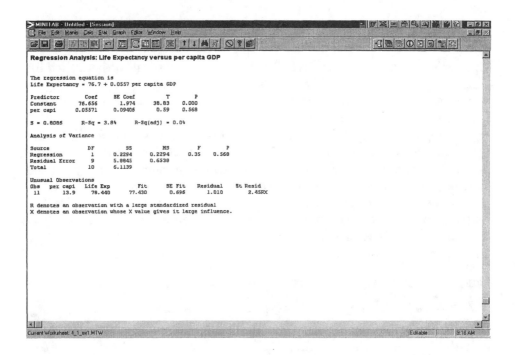

Near the bottom of the output, Obs 11 is identified as an unusual observation. Of course this refers to Greece since it is the 11th data point in the Minitab worksheet. The "X" at the end of the line indicates that Minitab has found that Greece is an 'influential observation'.

> ▸ **Problem 23 (pg. 234)** Kepler's Law of Planetary Motion

Open Minitab worksheet **4_3_23**. The distance from the sun should be in C2, and sidereal year should be in C3. First draw a scatter plot of the data. Click on **Graph→ Plot.** Select "Year" for the **Y**-variable and "Distance" for the **X**-variable. Enter an appropriate title (**Annotation→ Title)** and click on **OK** to view the scatter plot.

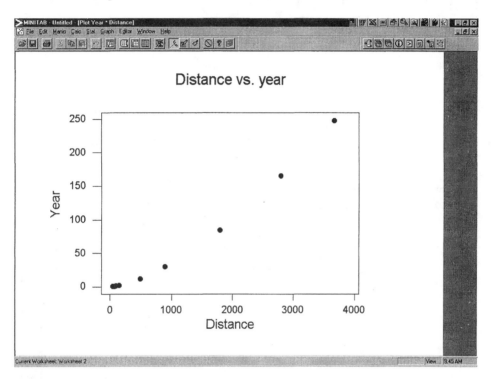

To do the regression analysis, first notice that "Distance" is the x-variable and "Year" is the y-variable. To find the least squares regression equation, click on **Stat → Regression → Regression.** Enter C2 for the **Response** variable, and C1 as the **Predictor.** Click on **Results.** If you would like to see the other regression output, then select **Regression equation, table of coefficients, s, R-squared, and basic analysis of variance.**   Finally, click on **Graphs** and enter C1 beneath **Residuals versus the variables**. Click on **OK** to view the regression analysis and the residual plot.

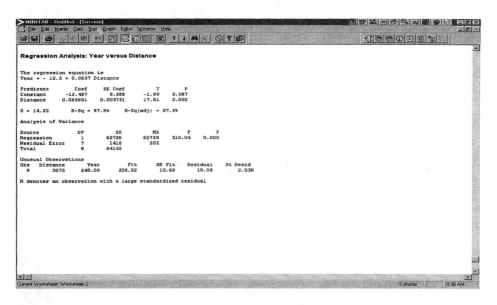

Notice that an Unusual Observation is reported. "Obs 9", which is Pluto, has a large standardized residual, which is indicated by the "R" at the end of the line. The regression equation is Year = -12.5 + 0.0657*Distance. Now look at the residual plot.

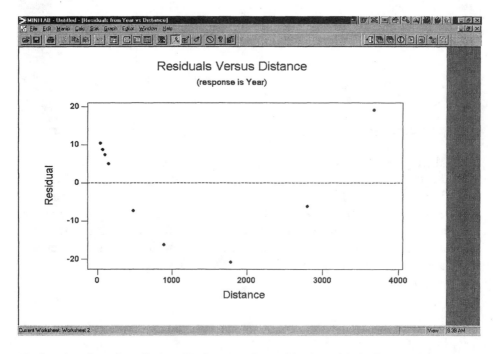

Notice that there is a distinct U-shape to the residuals. This indicates that the least squares regression line is not a good model for this data.

▶ Problem 27 (pg. 234)   Height vs. Weight

Open Minitab worksheet **4_3_27**. The Heights should be in C2, and Weight should be in C3. First draw a scatter plot of the data. Click on **Graph→ Plot.** Select "Weight" for the **Y**-variable and "Height" for the **X**-variable. Enter an appropriate title (**Annotation→ Title)** and click on **OK** to view the scatter plot.

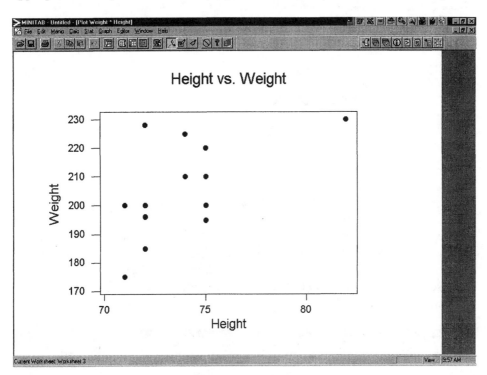

Notice that there is one data point that is far away from the other points. Run the regression to see if it is an "Unusual Observation". To find the least squares regression equation, click on **Stat → Regression → Regression.** Enter C3 for the **Response** variable, and C2 as the **Predictor.** Click on **Results.** If you would like to see the other regression output, then select **Regression equation, table of coefficients, s, R-squared, and basic analysis of variance.** Finally, click on **Graphs** and enter C2 beneath **Residuals versus the variables**. Click on **OK** to view the regression analysis and the residual plot.

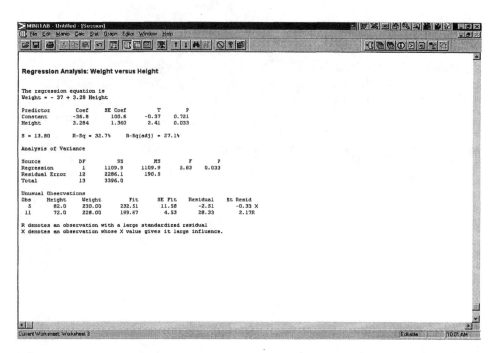

The regression equation is Weight = -37 + 3.28 * Height. There are 2 unusual observations: Observation 5 (Randy Johnson) has an X at the end of the line which indicates that it is an influential observation, and observation 11 (Pete Harnisch) has an R at the end of the line which indicates that is has a large standardized residual.

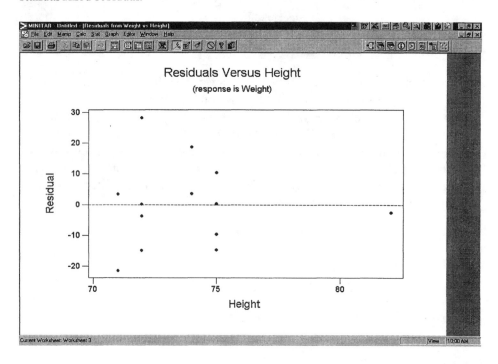

Notice that the residual corresponding to Randy Johnson is far to the right of the other residuals. Repeat the above steps after removing the data for Randy Johnson. The regression analysis will look like the following.

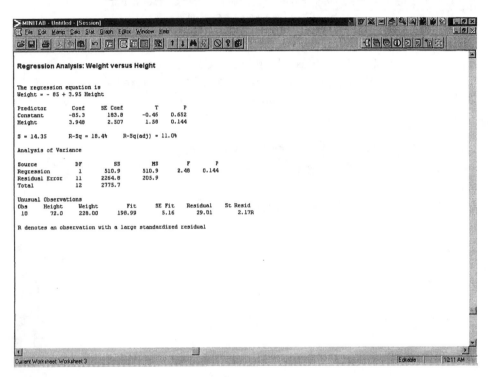

The regression equation changes to : Weight = -85 + 3.95 * Height. Pete Harnisch still shows up with a large standardized residual.

Section 4.4

▶ Example 4 (pg. 239) Finding the Curve of Best Fit to an
                        Exponential Model

Open worksheet **4_4_Ex4**. Year should be in C1, Index in C2, Closing Price in
C3. First plot the closing price versus the index. Click on **Graph → Plot** and
select Closing Price for the **Y**-variable and Index for the **X**-variable. Enter a title
(**Annotation → Title**). Click on **OK**.

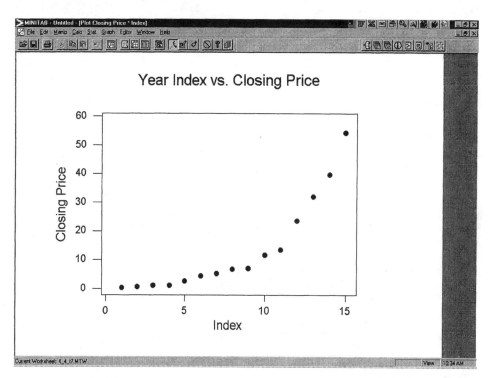

Notice that the data has a curved shape, indicating that it needs a transformation.
Close the scatter plot, so that you are back to the Session Window. To try the log
transformation, click on **Calc → Calculator. Store the result in** C4 and enter
the **Expression** "LOGT(c3)". Click on **OK** and C4 will contain the transformed
data. Name C4 "log(cp)" to indicate that it contains the log of the closing prices.

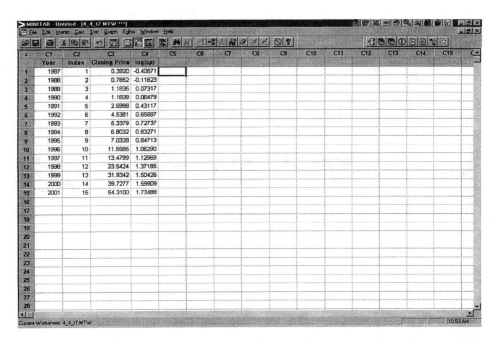

Create a new scatter plot. Click on **Graph** → **Plot** and select "log(cp)" for the **Y**-variable and Index for the **X**-variable. Enter a title (**Annotation** → **Title**). Click on **OK**.

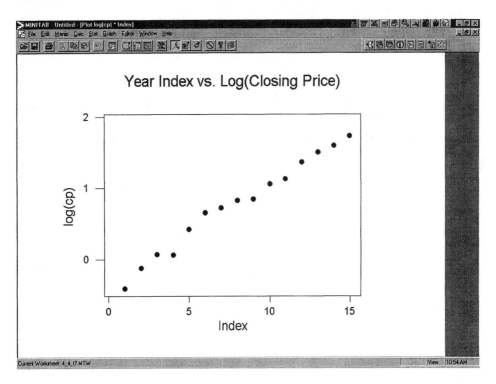

Notice that this scatter plot shows a linear relationship between the index and the transformed data. Now, find the regression equation. Click on **Stat** → **Regression** → **Regression.** Enter C4 for the **Response** variable, and enter C2 the **Predictors.** Click on **Results.** Since you would like to see the other regression output, then select **Regression equation, table of coefficients, s, R-squared, and basic analysis of variance.** Click on **OK** twice and view the output in the Session Window.

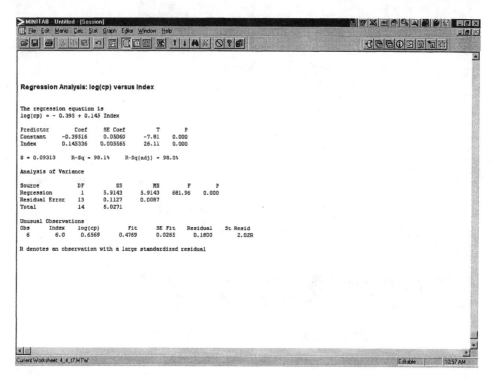

The regression equation is log(cp) = -.395 + .145*Index. You can now solve for a and b using a hand calculator.

▶ Example 5 (pg. 242) Finding the Curve of Best Fit to a Power
Model

Enter the data from Table 9 into a Minitab worksheet. Time should be in C1 and
Distance in C2. Click on **Graph → Plot** and select Distance for the **Y**-variable
and Time for the **X**-variable. Enter a title (**Annotation → Title**). Click on **OK**.

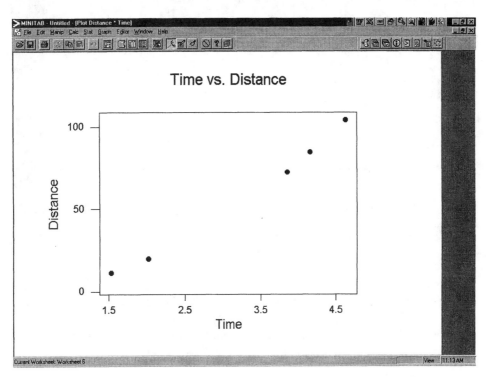

Now try a transformation. Close the scatter plot, so that you are back to the
Session Window. To try the log transformation, click on **Calc → Calculator.**
Store the result in C3 and enter the **Expression** "LOGT(c1)". Click on **OK** and
C3 will contain the transformed data. Name C3 "log(time)" to indicate that it
contains the log of the time. Repeat this step, so that you will have
"log(distance)" in C4. Create a scatter plot of the transformed data. Click on
Graph → Plot and select "log(Distance)" for the **Y**-variable and "log(Time)" for
the **X**-variable. Enter a title (**Annotation → Title**). Click on **OK**.

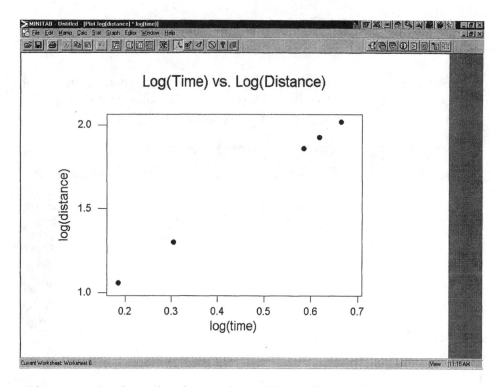

This scatter plot shows that the transformed data is linear. Now, do the regression analysis. Click on **Stat** → **Regression** → **Regression.** Enter C4 for the **Response** variable, and enter C3 as the **Predictors.** Click on **Results.** Since you would like to see the other regression output, then select **Regression equation, table of coefficients, s, R-squared, and basic analysis of variance.** Click on **OK** twice and view the output in the Session Window.

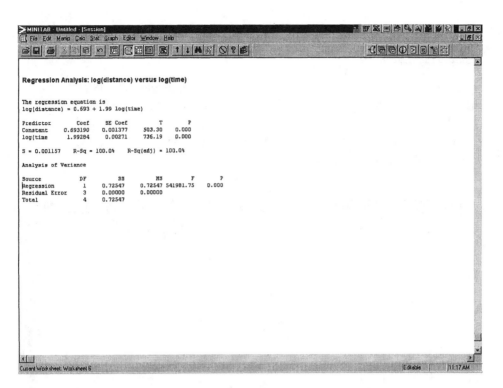

The regression equation is Log(distance) = .693 + 1.99 * Log(time). You can now solve for a and b using a hand calculator following the steps d and e on page 244 of the textbook.

> ▶ Problem 37 (pg. 246) Kepler's Law of Planetary Motion

Open Minitab worksheet **4_4_37** . The distance from the sun should be in C2, and sidereal year should be in C3. First draw a scatter plot of the data. Click on **Graph→ Plot.** Select "Year" for the Y-variable and "Distance" for the X-variable. Enter an appropriate title (**Annotation→ Title)** and click on **OK** to view the scatter plot.

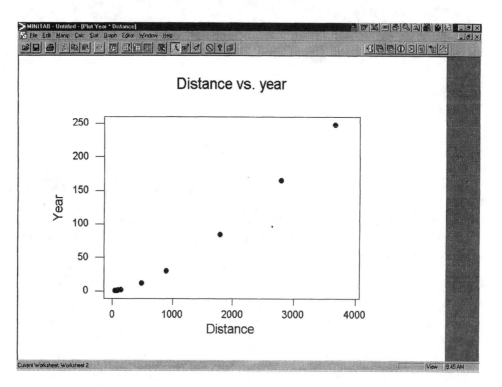

Notice the slight curve to the plot. Try a power transformation by calculating the log of both distance and year. Click on **Calc → Calculator. Store the result in** C4 and enter the **Expression** "LOGT(c2)". Click on **OK** and C4 will contain the transformed data. Name C4 "log(distance)" to indicate that it contains the log of the time. Repeat this step, so that you will have "log(year)" in C5.

Now, plot the transformed data. Click on **Graph→ Plot.** Select "Log(year)" for the **Y-**variable and "Log(distance)" for the **X-**variable. Enter an appropriate title (**Annotation→ Title)** and click on **OK** to view the scatter plot.

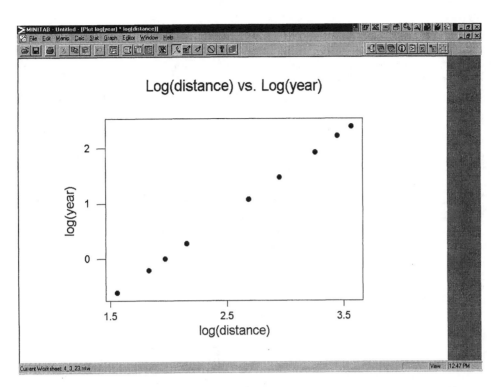

This scatter plot shows a linear relationship between the transformed variables. Now do the regression analysis on Log(distance) and Log(year). Click on **Stat → Regression → Regression.** Enter C5 for the **Response** variable, and enter C4 as the **Predictor.** Next, click on **Results.** Since you would like to see the other regression output, select **Regression equation, table of coefficients, s, R-squared, and basic analysis of variance.** Click on **OK** twice and view the output in the Session Window.

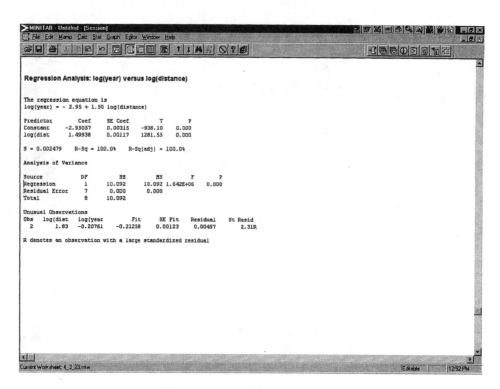

The regression equation is Log(Year) = -2.95 + 1.50 * Log(Distance). Use a hand calculator to find the power equation of best fit.

CHAPTER

5

Probability

Section 5.1

▶ Example 6 (pg. 269) Simulating Probabilities

To simulate the experiment of sampling 100 babies, let Minitab randomly
generate 100 1's and 0's. To do this, click on **Calc → Random data → Integer.**
You would like to **Generate** 100 **rows of data** and **Store in column** C1. Enter a
Minimum value of 0 (to represent a boy) and a **Maximum value** of 1 (to
represent a girl). Click on **OK** and you should see the random data in C1.

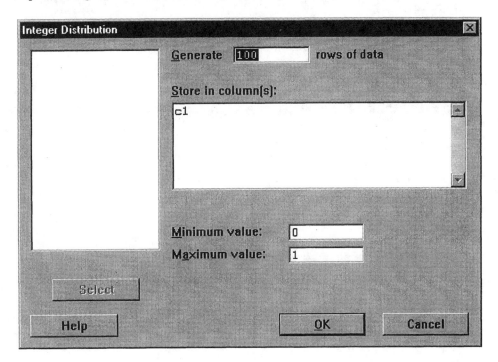

To count up the number of 1's and 0's, click on **Stat → Tables → Tally.** Select
C1 as the **Variable** and click on both **Counts** and **Percents.**

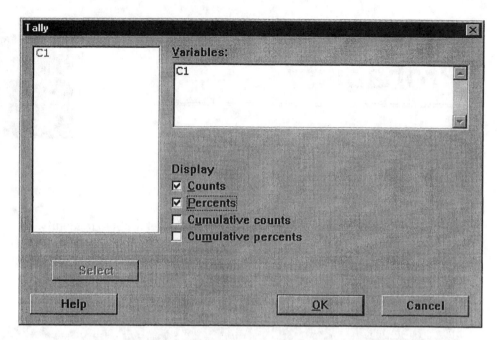

When you click on **OK,** the summary table will be in the Session Window.

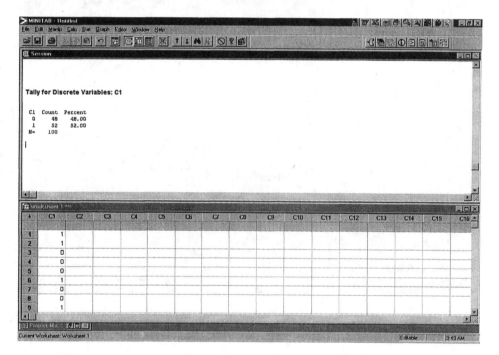

This random sample gave us 48% boys and 52% girls. Repeat these steps to generate a random sample of size 1000.

▶ **Problem 31 (pg. 274)** Simulation

To simulate the experiment of rolling a six-sided die 100 times, let Minitab randomly generate 100 integers with values 1 through 6. To do this, click on **Calc → Random data → Integer.** Since this simulation is repeated in part b, **Generate** 100 **rows of data** and **Store in column** C1-C2. Enter a **Minimum value** of 1 and a **Maximum value** of 6. Click on **OK** and you should see the random data in both C1 and C2. Repeat this step again, but this time **Generate** 500 **rows of data** and **Store in column** 3. Enter a **Minimum value** of 1 and a **Maximum value** of 6. To count up the results, click on **Stat → Tables → Tally.** Select C1-C3 as the **Variables** and click on both **Counts** and **Percents.**

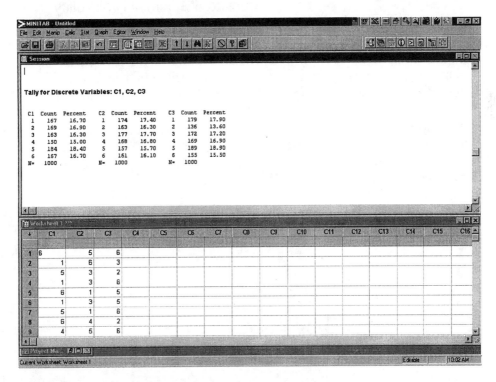

Notice that in the first sample there was 16.7% 1's, in the second sample there was 17.4% 1's, and in the third sample there was 17.9% 1's.

Discrete Probability Distributions

CHAPTER

6

Section 6.2

▶ Example 2 (pg. 341) Constructing a Binomial Probability Distribution

In this example, 6% of the human population is blood type O-negative and a random sample of size 4 is selected. Thus, you want to find the binomial probability distribution for n = 4 and p = .06. First, enter the X values 0, 1, 2, 3, and 4 in C1. Next, click on **Calc → Probability Distributions→ Binomial.** Since you want the probability for each value of X, select **Probability.** This tells MINITAB what type of calculation you want to do. The **Number of Trials** is 4 and the **Probability of Success** is .06. Enter C1 beside **Input Column.** Leave all other fields blank. Click on **OK.**

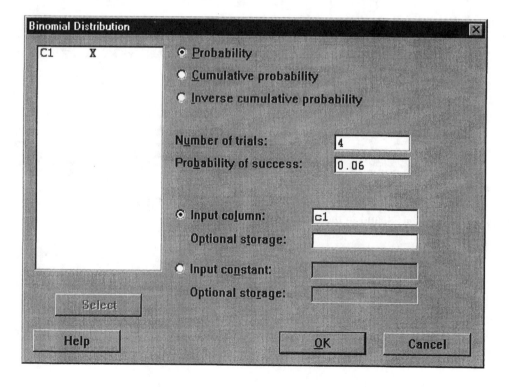

The binomial probability distribution for n=4 and p=.06 will be displayed in the Session Window. Notice that the probability that 2 people in a random sample of size 4 have blood type O-negative is .0191.

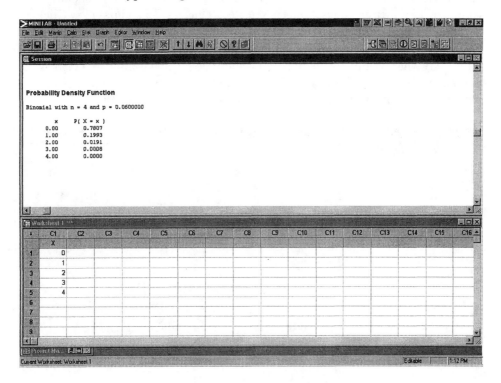

▶ Example 3 (pg. 344) Using the Binomial Distribution

In this example, 75% of American households have cable TV and a random sample of 15 American households is selected. Thus n = 15 and p = .75. Click on **Calc → Probability Distributions → Binomial.** To find the probability that exactly 10 of the 15 households have cable TV, select **Probability**. This tells MINITAB what type of calculation you want to do. The **Number of Trials** is 15 and the **Probability of Success** is .75. To find the probability of 10, enter 10 beside **Input Constant.** Leave all other fields blank. Click on **OK.**

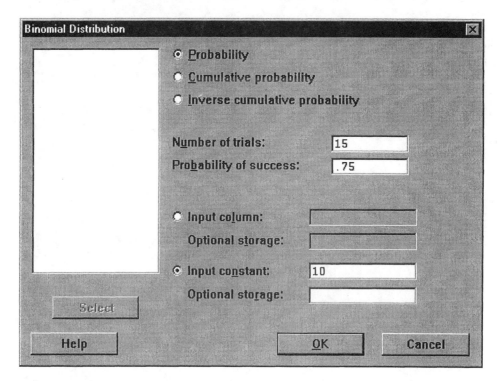

The probability that 10 of the 15 households sampled have cable TV will be displayed in the Session Window. Notice that the probability is .1651.

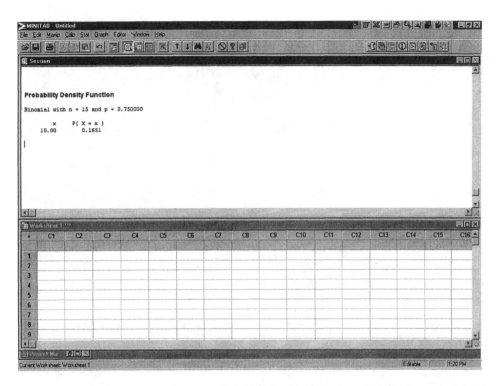

For part b, you want to find the probability that at least 13 of the 15 households have cable TV. One way to calculate this is to use the cumulative probability function. We will use this function to find the P(X ≤ 12), and then subtract the probability from 1 since we are interested in the complement of that probability. Click on **Calc → Probability Distributions→ Binomial.** To find the probability that 12 or less of the 15 households have cable TV, select **Cumulative Probability**. This tells MINITAB what type of calculation you want to do. The **Number of Trials** is 15 and the **Probability of Success** is .75. To find the probability of 12 or less, enter 12 beside **Input Constant.** Leave all other fields blank. Click on **OK.**

The probability that 12 or less of the 15 households sampled have cable TV will be displayed in the Session Window. Notice that the probability is .7639. (Notice that this is the probability that you are looking for in part c.)

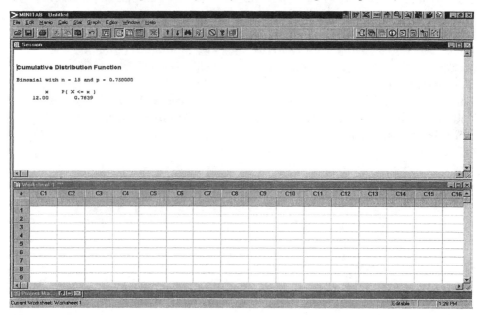

The probability that at least 13 households have cable TV is 1 - .7639 = .2361.

> ▶ Example 5 (pg. 346) Constructing Binomial Probability
>   Histograms

In order to graph the binomial distribution, you must first create the distribution
and save it in the Data Window. In C1, type in the values of X. Since n=10, the
values of X are 0, 1, 2, 3, 4, 5, 6, 7, 8, 9 and 10. Next, use MINITAB to generate
the binomial probabilities for n=10 and p=0.20. Click on **Calc**→ **Probability
Distributions** → **Binomial.** Select **Probability.** The **Number of Trials** is 10
and the **Probability of Success** is .20. Now, tell MINITAB that the X values are
in C1 and that you want the probabilities stored in C2. Enter C1 as the **Input
Column** and enter C2 for **Optional Storage.**

Click on **OK**. The probabilities should now be in C2. Label C1 as "X" and C2
as "P(X)". This will be helpful when you graph the distribution.

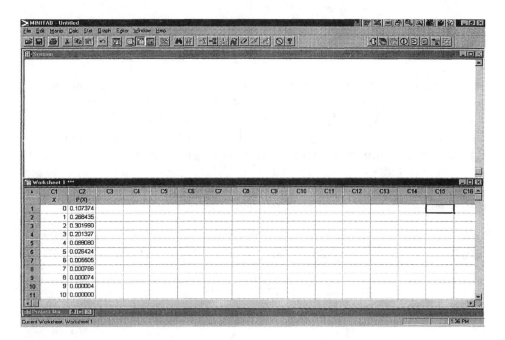

To create the graph, click on **Graph** → **Chart.** Enter C2 for the **Y** variable and C1 for the **X** variable. Leave **Function** blank. Click on **Annotation** → **Title** and enter an appropriate title to identify the binomial distribution. Click on **Edit Attributes** and enter a "1" for **Bar Width.** Click on **OK** twice to display the graph.

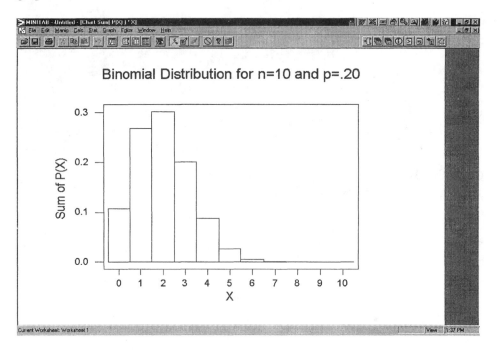

Repeat the steps above for parts b and c, changing the values of p.

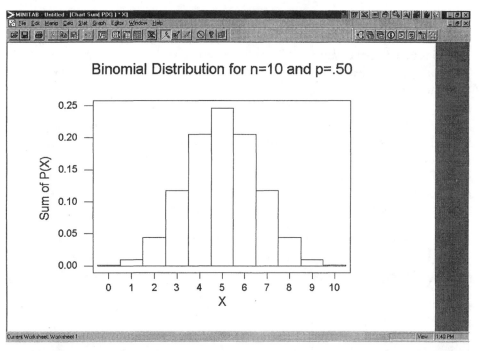

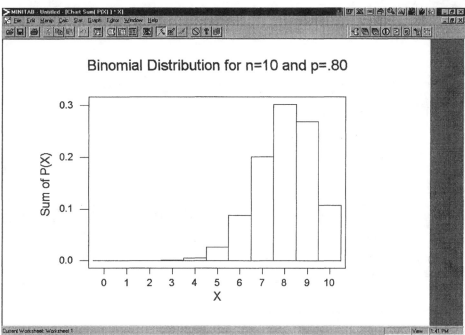

▶ Example 7 (pg. 350) Using the Binomial to Perform Inference

In 1998, 75% of American households had cable TV. Yolanda believes this percentage may have increased. In a random sample of 40 American households, she finds that 33 have cable TV. Thus n = 40 and p = .75. You want to find the probability that at least 33 of the 40 households have cable TV. One way to calculate this is to use the cumulative probability function. We will use this function to find the P(X ≤ 32), and then subtract the probability from 1 since we are interested in the complement of that probability. Click on **Calc →** **Probability Distributions → Binomial.** To find the probability that 32 or less of the 40 households have cable TV, select **Cumulative Probability**. This tells MINITAB what type of calculation you want to do. The **Number of Trials** is 40 and the **Probability of Success** is .75. To find the probability of 32 or less, enter 32 beside **Input Constant.** Leave all other fields blank. Click on **OK.**

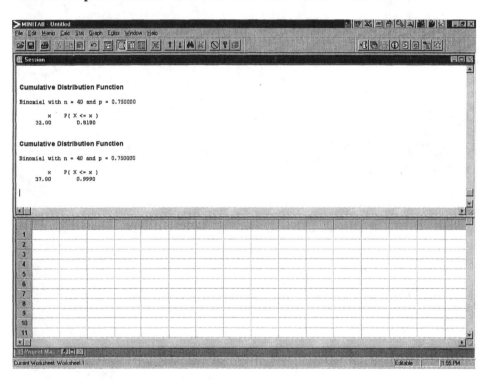

The output is in the Session Window. Notice the P(X ≤ 32) = .8180, so the P(X > 32) = 1 - .8180 = .1820.

Repeat the above steps for part b, to find P(X ≥ 38). Use 37 as the **Input Constant.** As you can see in the screen shot above, P(X ≤ 37) = .9990, so the P(X > 37) = 1 - .9990 = .001.

▶ Problem 25 (pg. 353)   Migraine Sufferers

In clinical trials, 2% of patients on Depakote experienced weight gain as a side effect. A random sample of 30 Depakote users is selected. Thus n = 30 and p = .02. Click on **Calc → Probability Distributions → Binomial.** To find the probability that exactly 3 of the 30 users had a weight gain, select **Probability**. This tells MINITAB what type of calculation you want to do. The **Number of Trials** is 30 and the **Probability of Success** is .02. To find the probability of 3, enter 3 beside **Input Constant.** Leave all other fields blank. Click on **OK** and the probability will be displayed in the Session Window.

For part b, you want to find the probability that 3 or fewer patients experienced weight gain as a side effect of using the drug. Repeat the steps above, but this time select **Cumulative Probability.** All other entries are the same. Click on **OK** and the probability will be displayed in the Session Window.

For part c, you want to find the probability that 4 or more patients experienced this side effect. Since $P(X \geq 4) = 1 - P(X \leq 3)$, you can use the output from part b and subtract from 1.

For part d, you want to find the probability that between 1 and 4 patients experienced this side effect. One way to calculate this is to find $P(X \leq 4)$ and subtract $P(X = 0)$. Click on **Calc → Probability Distributions → Binomial.** To find the probability that 4 or fewer of the 30 users had a weight gain, select **Cumulative Probability**. This tells MINITAB what type of calculation you want to do. The **Number of Trials** is 30 and the **Probability of Success** is .02. To find the probability of 4 or less, enter 4 beside **Input Constant.** Leave all other fields blank. Click on **OK** and the probability will be displayed in the Session Window. Now, click on **Calc → Probability Distributions → Binomial.** To find the probability that exactly 0 of the 30 users had a weight gain, select **Probability**. This tells MINITAB what type of calculation you want to do. The **Number of Trials** is 30 and the **Probability of Success** is .02. To find the probability of 0, enter 0 beside **Input Constant.** Leave all other fields blank. Click on **OK** and the probability will be displayed in the Session Window.

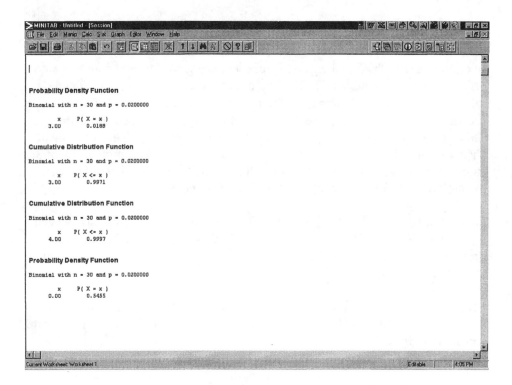

Use the probabilities shown in the Session Window to find the solutions to parts a - d.

a.   .0188
b.   .9971
c.   1 - .9971 = .0029
d.   .9997 - .5455 = .4542

▶ Problem 41 (pg. 355)   Simulation

There is a 98% chance that a 20-year-old male will survive to age 30. To simulate 100 random samples of size 30 from this population, click on **Calc** → **Random Data** → **Binomial. Generate** 100 **rows of data,** and **store in column** C1. The **Number of trials** is 30 and the **Probability of success** is .98. Click on OK and C1 should have the number of survivors for each of the 100 random samples in it. (Note: since this is random data, your results will be different from those shown below.)

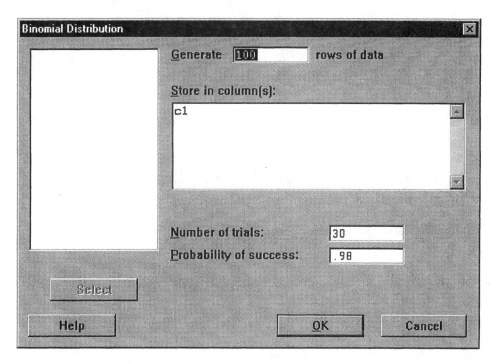

To find the probability that exactly 29 of the 30 males survived to age 30, click on **Stat**→ **Tables** → **Tally.** Select C1 as the **Variable**, and select both **Counts** and **Percents.** Click on OK and a summary of the data in C1 will be displayed in the Session Window.

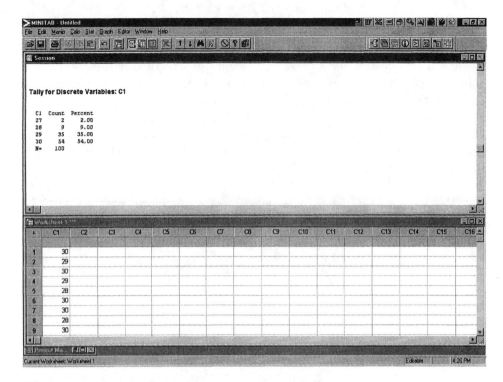

Notice that 35% of the time, 29 out of the 30 males survived. Thus, based on the simulation, the probability that 29 out of 30 males survive to age 30 is 0.35.

For part c, you want to find the exact probability based on the binomial distribution with n = 30 and p = .98. Click on **Calc → Probability Distributions → Binomial.** To find the probability that exactly 29 of the 30 males survive, select **Probability**. This tells MINITAB what type of calculation you want to do. The **Number of Trials** is 30 and the **Probability of Success** is .98. Enter 29 beside **Input Constant** and leave all other fields blank. Click on **OK** and the probability will be displayed in the Session Window. As you can see below, the theoretical probability is .3340.

Probability Density Function

```
Binomial with n = 30 and p = 0.980000

        x        P( X = x )
    29.00          0.3340
```

For part d, you want to find the probability that at most 27 males survived. According to the summary table from the simulation, only 2% of the time did at most 27 survive.

To find the theoretical probability that at most 27 survive, repeat the steps for part c, but this time select **Cumulative Probability** and enter 27 beside **Input Constant.** All other entries are the same. Click on **OK** and the probability will be displayed in the Session Window.

Cumulative Distribution Function

```
Binomial with n = 30 and p = 0.980000

        x     P( X <= x )
    27.00        0.0217
```

As you can see, the probability is .0217.

Finally, to find the mean number of survivors based on the simulations, click on **Stat→ Basic Statistics→ Display Descriptive Statistics.** Select C1 for the **Variable.**

Descriptive Statistics: C1

Variable SE Mean	N	Mean	Median	TrMean	StDev
C1 0.074	100	29.410	30.000	29.478	0.740

Variable	Minimum	Maximum	Q1	Q3
C1	27.000	30.000	29.000	30.000

The mean number of survivors from the simulation is 29.41. The theoretical mean number of survivors is 30 * .98 = 29.4. Thus, this simulation gave results which are very close to the theoretical results.

Section 6.3

▶ Example 2 (pg. 359) Finding Poisson Probabilities

Since cars arrive at McDonald's at a rate of 2 cars per minute, $\lambda = 2$ for this Poisson example. To find the probability that 6 cars arrive between 12:00 and 12:05, notice that this is a time interval of 5 minutes. This means that an average of (2)(5)=10 cars will arrive in a 5 minute interval. Click on **Calc→ Probability Distributions → Poisson.** Since you want a simple probability, select **Probability** and enter 10 for the **Mean.** To find the probability that X=6, enter 6 for the **Input constant.**

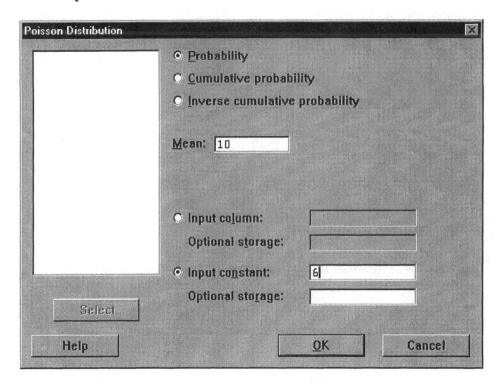

Click on **OK** and the probability will be in the Session Window.

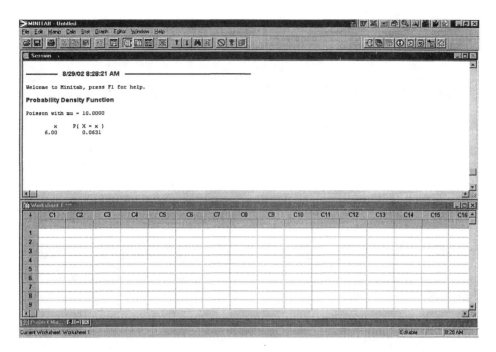

Now, to find the probability that fewer than 6 cars arrive in the 5-minute interval, repeat the steps above. Click on **Calc → Probability Distributions → Poisson.** This time you want a cumulative probability, so select **Cumulative Probability** and enter 10 for the **Mean.** To find the probability that X < 6, enter 5 for the **Input constant.**

When you click on **OK**, the results will be in the Session Window.

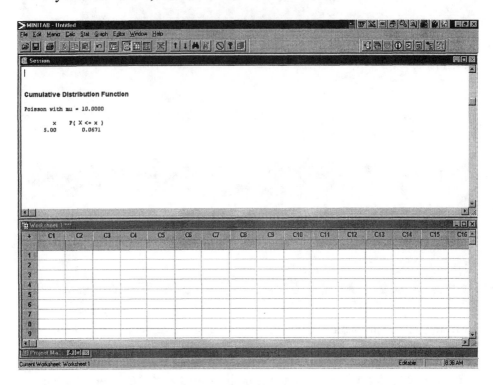

Finally, to find the probability that at least 6 cars arrive in the 5-minute interval, just use $1 - P(X < 6) = 1 - .0671 = .9329$.

▶ Example 4 (pg. 363)   Do Beetles follow a Poisson Distribution?

In this example, you want to compare the actual number of beetles to the expected number of beetles (assuming a Poisson distribution with $\mu=10$). First, create the Poisson distribution and save it in the Data Window. To do this, type the values of X into C1. Since n=22, the values of X are 0, 1, 2, 3, 4, 5, ...22. Next, use MINITAB to generate the Poisson probabilities for n=22 and $\mu=10$. Click on **Calc** → **Probability Distributions** → **Poisson.** Select **Probability.** The **Mean** is 10. Now, tell MINITAB that the X values are in C1 and that you want the probabilities stored in C2. Enter C1 as the **Input Column** and enter C2 for **Optional Storage.**

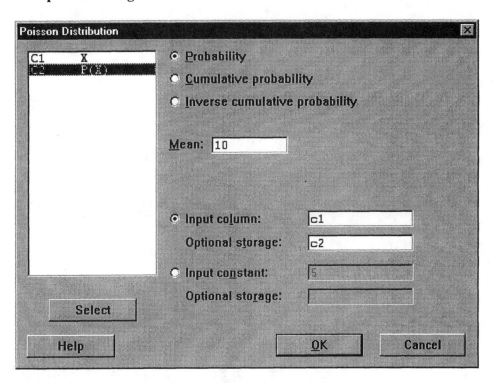

Click **OK.** The probabilities are in C2 of the Data Window. Notice, for example, that P(X=4) = .018917.

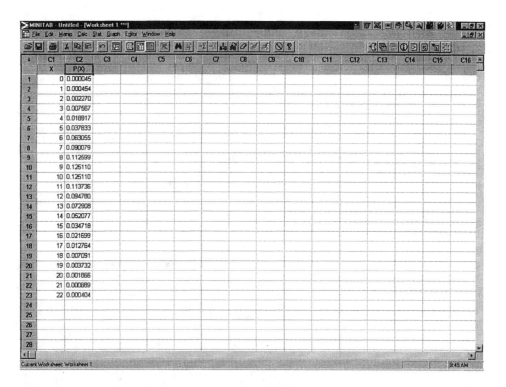

Next, multiply each probability in C2 by 200. Click on **Calc → Calculator**.
Store result in variable C3 and type in the **Expression** 200*C2.

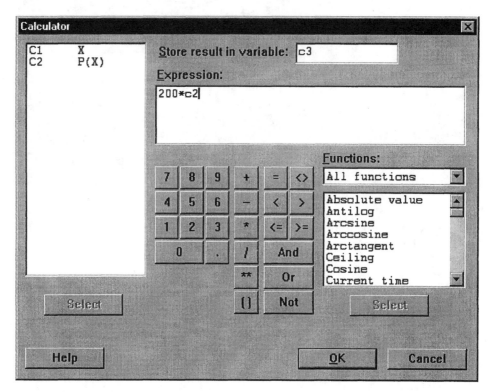

ction 6.3 153

Click on **OK** and the expected number of beetles will be C3.

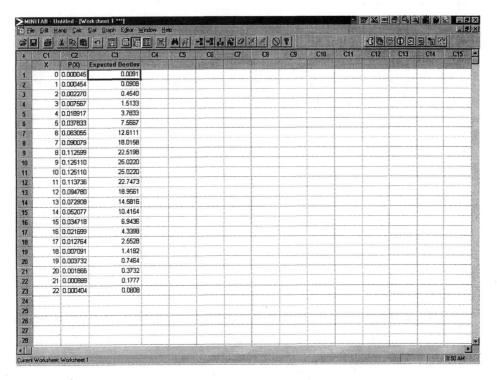

You can now compare the actual number of beetles to the expected number of beetles.

▶ Problem 15 (pg. 367) Wendy's Drive-Through

Since cars arrive at Wendy's at a rate of 0.2 cars per minute, $\lambda = 2$ for this Poisson example. To find the probability distribution of the number that arrive between 12:00 and 12:30, notice that this is a time interval of 30 minutes. This means that an average of (.2)(30)=6 cars will arrive in a 30 minute interval. First, create the Poisson distribution and save it in the Data Window. To do this, open Minitab Worksheet **6_3_15**. The X values are in C1 and C2 contains the official count of arrivals. Next, use MINITAB to generate the Poisson probabilities for n=16 and μ=6. Click on **Calc → Probability Distributions → Poisson.** Select **Probability**. The **Mean** is 6. Now, tell MINITAB that the X values are in C1 and that you want the probabilities stored in C3. Enter C1 as the **Input Column** and enter C3 for **Optional Storage.** Click on OK and the probability distribution will be in C3. To find the expected number of arrivals, notice that there are 200 Wendy's restaurants. So multiply each probability in C3 by 200. Click on **Calc → Calculator. Store result in variable C4** and type in the **Expression** 200*C3.

Now compare the numbers in C2 to the numbers in C4.

	C1	C2	C3	C4
	x (number of cars arriving)	Frequency	P(x)	Expected
1	1	4	0.014873	2.9745
2	2	5	0.044618	8.9235
3	3	13	0.089235	17.8470
4	4	23	0.133853	26.7705
5	5	25	0.160623	32.1246
6	6	28	0.160623	32.1246
7	7	25	0.137677	27.5354
8	8	27	0.103258	20.6515
9	9	21	0.068838	13.7677
10	10	15	0.041303	8.2606
11	11	5	0.022529	4.5058
12	12	3	0.011264	2.2529
13	13	2	0.005199	1.0398
14	14	2	0.002228	0.4456
15	15	0	0.000891	0.1783
16	16	2	0.000334	0.0668

▶ Problem 21 (pg. 368) Simulation

Since the rate of colds is 23.8 per 100 18 to 24 year olds, $\lambda = 23.8$ for this Poisson example. To find the expected number of colds per 500 people in this age group, just multiply 23.8 by 5. This means that there is an average of (23.8)(5)=119 colds per 500 people. To simulate taking 100 random samples of size 500, click on **Calc → Random Data → Poisson. Generate** 100 **rows of data** and **Store in column** C1. Enter 119 for the **Mean**.

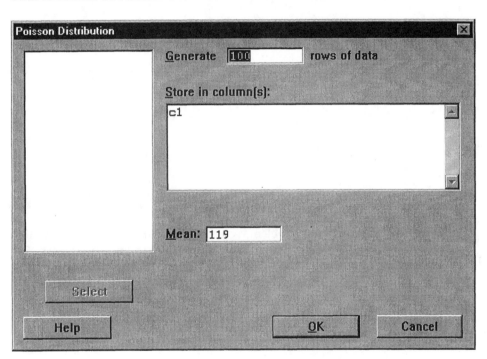

Click on OK and the random data will be in C1. Now summarize the random data by creating a table of the results. Click on **Stat→ Tables → Tally.** Enter C1 for the **Variable,** and select both **Counts** and **Percents.** The summary table will be in the Session Window. Since this is random data, everyone's summary table will be a little different.

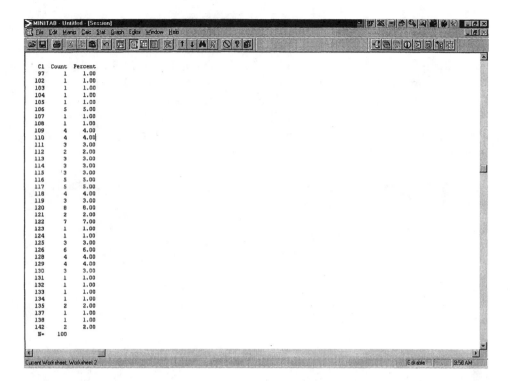

To answer parts c and d of this problem, you can use the table above. Notice that the value of 150 *never* appears in the data. Thus the probability that at least 150 people in a group of 500 will have a cold is 0. Also, notice that there is one value less than 100 -- that is 97. Thus the $P(X < 100) = 1/100 = .01$. Next, calculate the mean, standard deviation, and 5-number summary of the data. Click on **Stat → Basic Statistics → Display Descriptive Statistics.** Select C1 and click on **OK**. The results will be in the Session Window.

Descriptive Statistics: C1

Variable	N	Mean	Median	TrMean	StDev	SE Mean
C1	100	119.20	119.00	119.06	9.25	0.92

Variable	Minimum	Maximum	Q1	Q3
C1	97.00	142.00	112.25	126.00

Normal Probability Distribution

CHAPTER

7

Section 7.1

▶ Problem 23 (pg. 391) Hitting with a Pitching Wedge

Open Minitab worksheet **7_1_23**. The distances should be C1. To draw a histogram with a normal curve superimposed over it, click on **Stat→ Basic Statistics → Display Descriptive Statistics.** Select C1 for the variable, and then click on **Graphs.** Select **Histogram of data, with normal curve.**

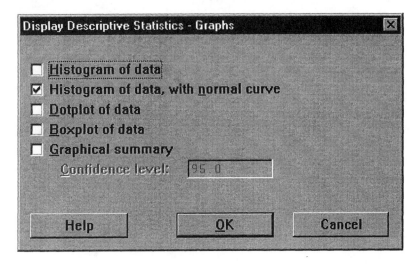

Click on **OK** twice to view the graph.

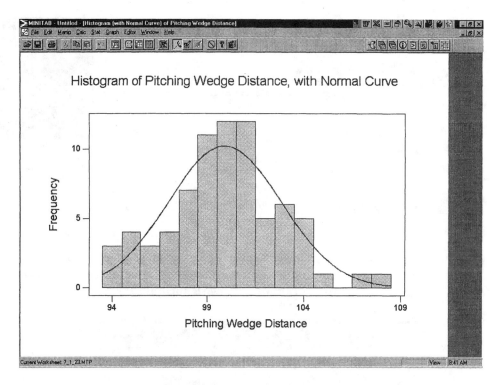

Use the graph to help you decide if the data follows a normal distribution.

Section 7.3

▶ Example 1 (pg. 406) Finding Area under a Normal Curve

The height of 3 year old girls is normally distributed with μ=38.72 and
σ=3.17. What percent of 3 year old girls have a height less than 35 inches? To
do this in MINITAB, click on **Calc → Probability Distributions → Normal.**
On the input screen, select **Cumulative probability.** (Cumulative probability
'accumulates' all probability to the left of the input constant.) Enter 38.72 for the
Mean and 3.17 for the **Standard deviation.** Next select **Input Constant** and
enter the value 35.

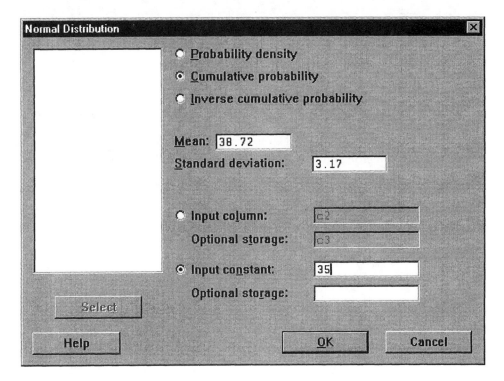

Click on **OK** and the probability should be displayed in the Session Window.

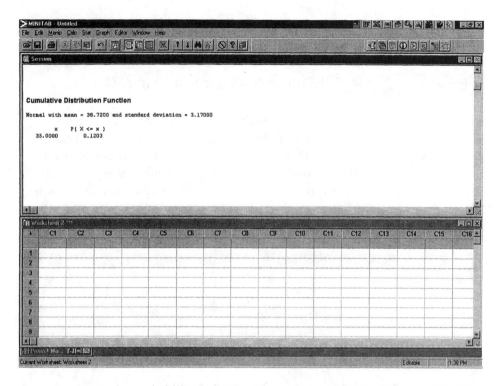

As you can see, the probability is .1203. Thus, about 12.03% of 3-year-old girls have a height of less than 35 inches.

▶ Example 2 (pg. 408) Height of 3 year old girls

Heights are normally distributed with $\mu=38.72$ inches and $\sigma=3.17$ inches. To find $P(35 \le X \le 40)$, you will need MINITAB to give you two probabilities: one using X=40 and the other using X=35. Click on **Calc → Probability Distributions → Normal.** On the input screen, select **Cumulative probability.** Enter 38.72 for the **Mean** and 3.17 for the **Standard deviation.** Next select **Input Constant** and enter the value 40. Click on **OK.** Repeat the above steps using an **Input constant** of 35. Now the Session Window should have $P(X \le 40)$ and $P(X \le 35)$.

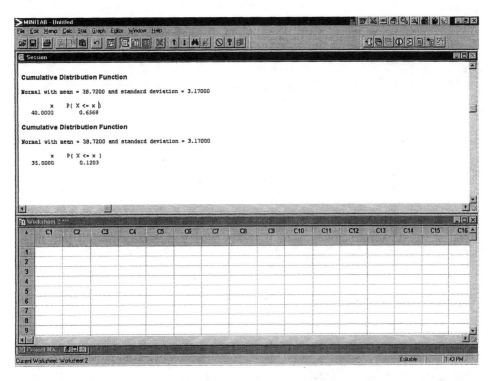

So, to find the $P(35 \le X \le 40)$, you must subtract the two probabilities. Thus, the $P(35 \le X \le 40) = .6568 - .1203 = .5365$. (Note: Minitab uses more decimal places than the textbook does so this answer is a little different.)

▶ Example 3 (pg. 409) Finding a specific data value

Heights are normally distributed with μ=38.72 inches and σ=3.17 inches. Find
the height of a 3 year old at the 20th percentile. To do this in MINITAB, click on
Calc → Probability Distributions → Normal. On the input screen, select
Inverse Cumulative probability. Enter 38.72 for the **Mean** and 3.17 for the
Standard deviation. For this type of problem, the **Input constant** will be the
area to the left of the X-value we are looking for. This input constant will be a
decimal number between 0 and 1. For this example, select **Input Constant** and
enter the value .20 since 20% of the heights are below this number. Click on **OK**
and the X-value should be in the Session Window. Notice that the 20th percentile
of heights of 3 year old girls is 36.0521 inches.

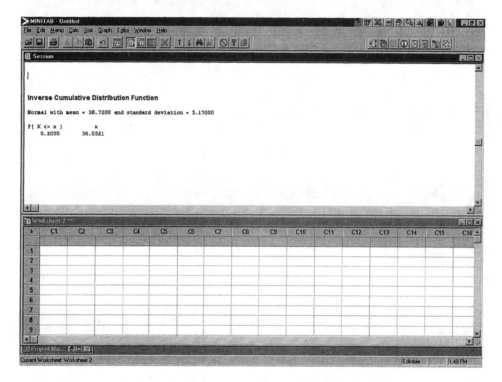

> ▶ Example 4 (pg. 410) Finding a specific data value

Heights are normally distributed with $\mu=38.72$ inches and $\sigma=3.17$ inches. Find the heights of 3 year old girls that separate the middle 98% of the distribution from the top and bottom 1%. To do this in MINITAB, click on **Calc** → **Probability Distributions** → **Normal.** On the input screen, select **Inverse Cumulative probability.** Enter 38.72 for the **Mean** and 3.17 for the **Standard deviation.** For this type of problem, the **Input constant** will be the area to the left of the X-value we are looking for. This input constant will be a decimal number between 0 and 1. For this example, select **Input Constant** and enter the value .99 since 99% of the heights are below the top 1%. Click on **OK** and the X-value should be in the Session Window. Repeat this step to find the bottom 1% cutoff point, but this time enter the value .01 as the **Input Constant.**

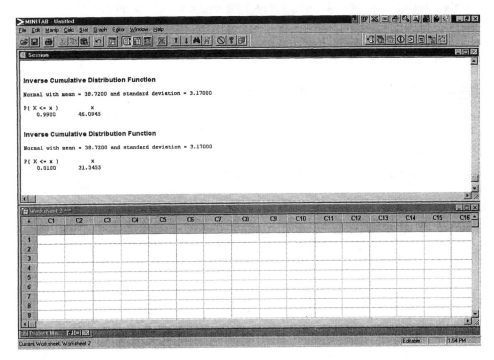

Notice that the 99th percentile of heights of 3 year old girls is 46.0945 inches and the 1st percentile of heights is 31.3455.

▶ Problem 11 (pg. 411) Serum Cholesterol

HDL cholesterol of females 20-29 years old is normally distributed with μ=53 and σ=13.4. For each of the parts a through e, click on **Calc → Probability Distributions → Normal.** On the input screen for each part, select **Cumulative probability.** Enter 53 for the **Mean** and 13.4 for the **Standard deviation.**

(a) Next select **Input Constant** and enter the value 39. Click on **OK.** (.1481)
(b) Next select **Input Constant** and enter the value 71. Click on **OK.** To find the probability that HDL is above 71, subtract the probability in the Session Window from 1. (1 - .9104 = .0896)
(c) Next select **Input Constant** and enter the value 75. Click on **OK.** Repeat with an **Input Constant** of 60. Click on **OK.** Subtract the two probabilities. (.9497 - .6993 = .2504)
(d) Next select **Input Constant** and enter the value 45. Click on **OK.** (.2752)
(e) Next select **Input Constant** and enter the value 60. Click on **OK.** Repeat with an **Input Constant** of 50. Click on **OK.** Subtract the two probabilities. (.6993 - .4114 = .2879)

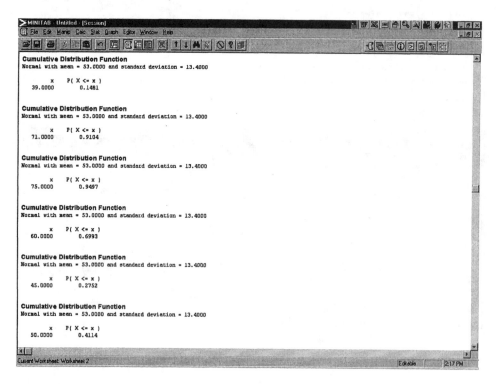

▶ Problem 21 (pg. 412) Finding a specific data value

 HDL cholesterol of females 20-29 years old is normally distributed with μ=53 and σ=13.4. Find the given percentiles of HDL levels. To do this in MINITAB, click on **Calc → Probability Distributions → Normal.** On the input screen, select **Inverse Cumulative probability.** Enter 53 for the **Mean** and 13.4 for the **Standard deviation.** For this type of problem, the **Input constant** will be the area to the left of the X-value we are looking for. This input constant will be a decimal number between 0 and 1.

(a) For this part, you are looking for the 25th percentile. Select **Input Constant** and enter the value .25 since 25% of the HDL levels are below the number we are looking for. Click on **OK** and the X-value should be in the Session Window. (43.9618)

(c) To find the cholesterol levels that make up the middle 80%. This area is between the 90th and 10th percentile. Select **Input Constant** and enter the value .90 since 90% of the HDL levels are below the number we are looking for. Click on **OK** and the X-value should be in the Session Window. Repeat this step, but enter the value .10 since there are 10% of the HDL levels below the number we are looking for. (70.1728, 35.8272)

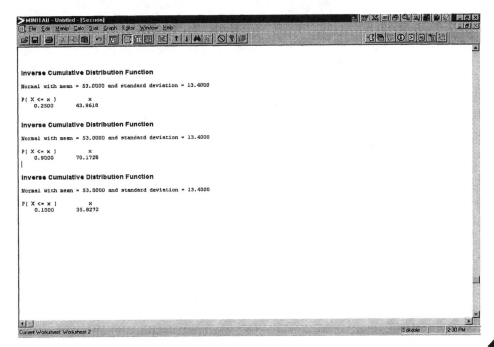

Section 7.4

▶ Example 3 (pg. 419) Assessing Normality

Open Minitab worksheet **7_4_EX3**. The waiting times are in C1. To draw a normal probability plot, click on **Graph → Probability Plot.** Select C1 for the **Variable** and be sure that the **Distribution** is Normal.

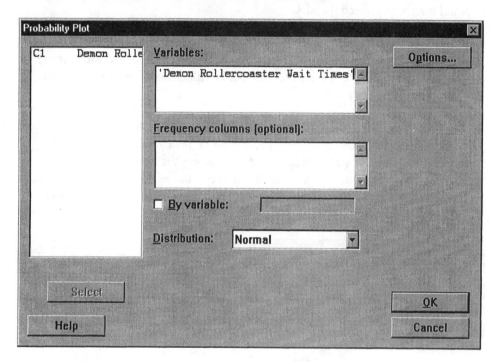

Click on **OK** and the normal probability plot should appear.

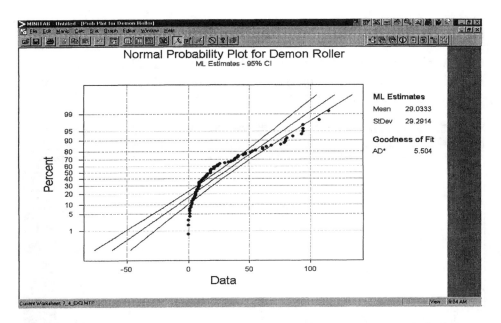

Clearly the normal probability plot is not linear. Thus, you can conclude that waiting times are not normally distributed.

> ▶ Problem 9 (pg. 421)   Volume of Philip Morris Stock

Open Minitab worksheet **7_4_9**. The stock volumes are in C1. To draw a
normal probability plot, click on **Graph → Probability Plot.** Select C1 for the
Variable and be sure that the **Distribution** is Normal.

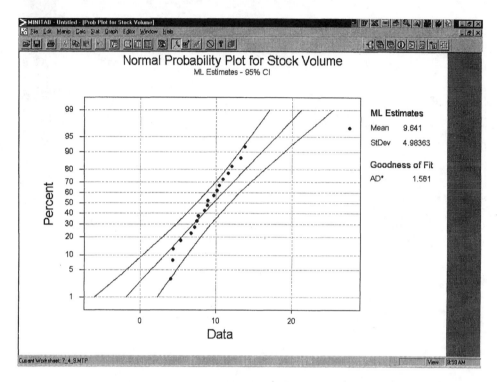

Notice that there is one data point outside of the bounds, and one that is right on
the bound. Thus, you would conclude that the data is not normally distributed.

Section 7.5

▶ **Example 2 (pg. 425)** Sampling Distribution of the Sample Mean

The height of 3 year old girls is normally distributed with μ=38.72 and σ=3.17. Approximate the sampling distribution of $\bar{x}$ by taking 100 simple random samples of size n = 5. To do this in MINITAB, click on **Calc → Random Data → Normal. Generate** 100 **rows of data** and **Store in columns** C1-C5. Enter the 38.72 for the **Mean** and 3.17 for the **Standard deviation.**

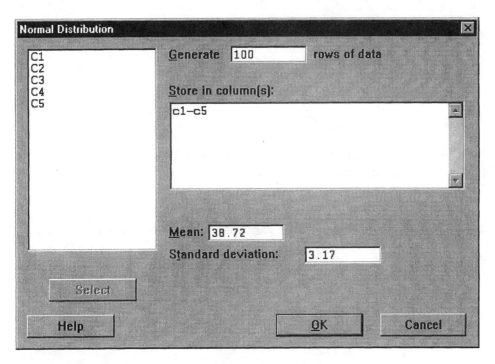

Click on **OK**. There will be 100 rows and 5 columns of random data in the Minitab worksheet. Each row represents a sample of size n=5. Since this is random data, everyone's data will be different.

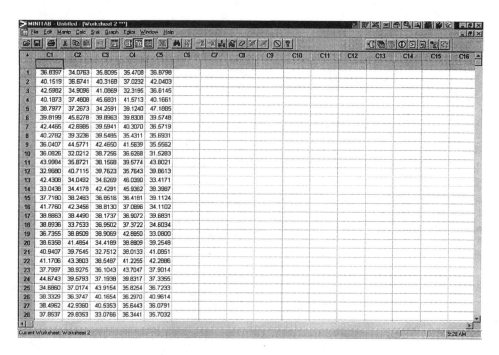

Next, calculate the mean of each of the samples. Click on **Calc**→ **Row Statistics.** Click on **Mean,** select **Input variables** C1-C5 and **Store result in** C6.

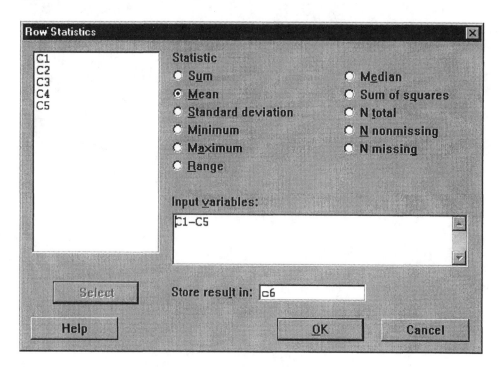

Click on **OK** and C6 will contain the averages for each row of 5 data points.

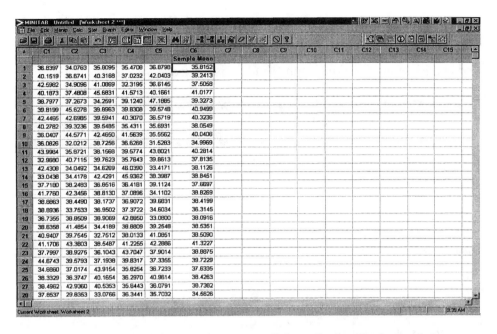

To draw a histogram of the sample means, click on **Stat → Basic Statistics →
Display Descriptive Statistics.** Select C6 for the **Variable** and click on **Graphs**.
Select **Histogram of Data** and click on **OK** twice to view the histogram.

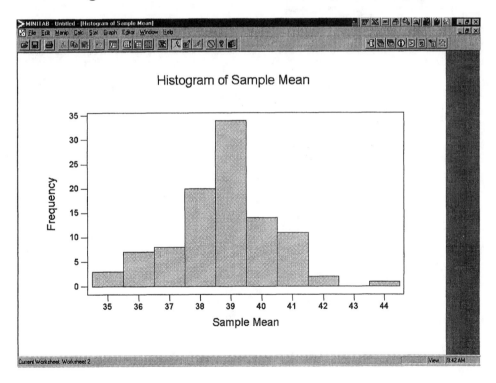

The descriptive statistics of the sample means are in the Session Window and can be seen after the Graph Window is closed.

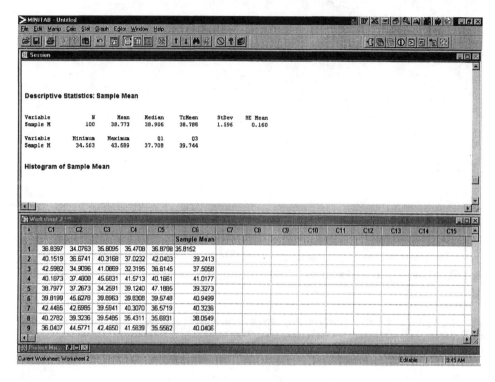

Notice that the mean of the 100 sample means is 38.773 and the standard deviation is 1.596.

▶ Example 4 (pg. 431) Describing the Sampling Distribution

The height of 3 year old girls is normally distributed with μ=38.72 and σ=3.17. Compute the probability that a random sample of size n=10 results in a sample mean greater than 40 inches. To find the probability that the *mean* height of 10 girls is more than 40 inches, you will need to calculate the standard deviation of $\bar{x}$ which is equal to $3.17/\sqrt{10}$ = 1.00. (Use a hand calculator for this calculation.) Now let MINITAB do the rest for you. Click on **Calc → Probability Distributions → Normal.** On the input screen, select **Cumulative probability.** Enter 38.72 for the **Mean** and 1.00 for the **Standard deviation.** Next select **Input Constant** and enter the value 40. Click on **OK** and the probability should appear in the Session Window.

Cumulative Distribution Function

```
Normal with mean = 38.7200 and standard deviation = 1.00000

        x      P( X <= x )
   40.0000        0.8997
```

Since you want to know the probability that the mean height is greater than 40, you should subtract this probability from 1. So 1 - .8997 = .1003.

> ▶ Example 5 (pg. 431) Sampling from a non-Normal Population

This time the population is the Exponential Distribution with mean and standard deviation equal to 10. Approximate the sampling distribution of $\bar{x}$ by taking 300 simple random samples of size n = 3, n=12, and n=30. To do this in MINITAB, you will repeat the following steps three times, once for each value of n. Click on **Calc → Random Data → Exponential. Generate** 300 **rows of data** and **Store in columns** C1-C3. Enter 10 for the **Mean**.

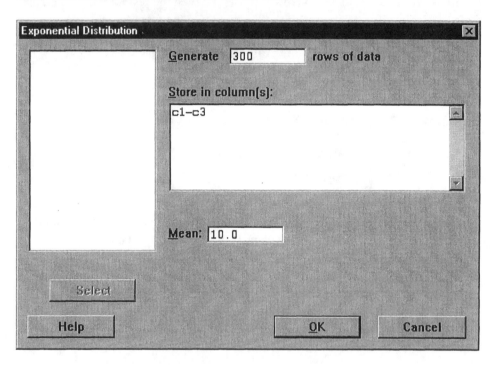

Click on **OK**. There will be 300 rows and 3 columns of random data in the Minitab worksheet. Each row represents a sample of size n=3. Since this is random data, everyone's data will be different. Next, calculate the mean of each of the samples. Click on **Calc → Row Statistics.** Click on **Mean,** select **Input variables** C1-C3 and **Store result in** C4. Click on **OK** and C4 will contain the averages for each row of 3 data points.

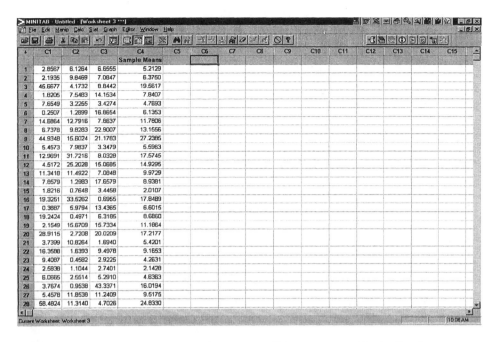

To draw a histogram of the sample means, click on **Stat → Basic Statistics → Display Descriptive Statistics.** Select C4 for the **Variable** and click on **Graphs.** Select **Histogram of Data** and click on **OK** twice to view the histogram.

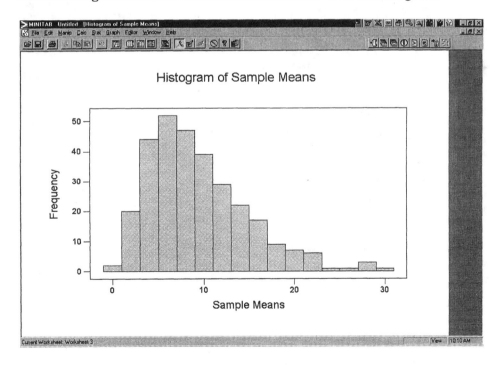

Notice that the histogram is still very skewed, just like the original population. The descriptive statistics of the sample means are in the Session Window and can be seen after the Graph Window is closed.

Descriptive Statistics: Sample Means

Variable	N	Mean	Median	TrMean	StDev	SE Mean
Sample	300	9.362	8.396	8.996	5.471	0.316

Variable	Minimum	Maximum	Q1	Q3
Sample M	0.355	29.025	5.313	12.449

Notice that the mean of the 300 sample means is 9.362 and the standard deviation is 8.396. Now repeat this for n=12. This time when you generate the random samples, you should **Store in columns** C1-C12.

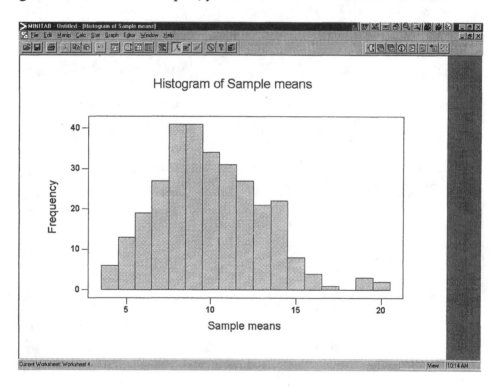

Descriptive Statistics: Sample means

Variable	N	Mean	Median	TrMean	StDev	SE Mean
Sample	300	9.893	9.628	9.801	3.056	0.176

Variable	Minimum	Maximum	Q1	Q3
Sample	3.914	20.324	7.660	11.959

Notice that the histogram is not as skewed as before and the mean is 9.893, but this time the standard deviation is 3.056 -- much smaller than last time.

Now repeat this again for n=30. This time when you generate the random samples, you should **Store in columns** C1-C30.

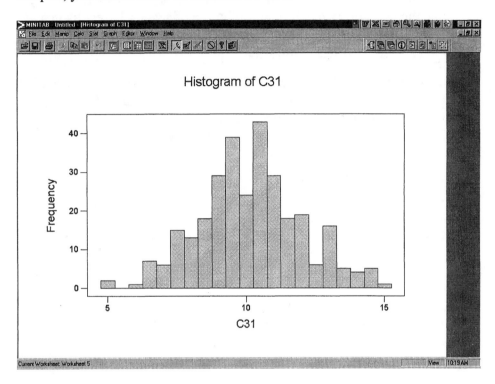

Descriptive Statistics: C31

Variable	N	Mean	Median	TrMean	StDev	SE Mean
C31	300	10.135	10.145	10.122	1.821	0.105

Variable	Minimum	Maximum	Q1	Q3
C31	4.977	15.181	8.995	11.175

For n=30, the histogram has become fairly symmetric. The mean is 10.145 and notice that the standard deviation is now a very small 1.821.

▶ Example 6 (pg. 433) Applying the Central Limit Theorem

The mean calorie intake of males 20-39 years old is μ=2716 with σ=72.8. Compute the probability that a random sample of size n=35 results in a sample mean greater than 2750. To find the probability that the *mean* calorie intake is more than 2750, you will need to calculate the standard deviation of $\bar{x}$, which is equal to $72.8 / \sqrt{35}$ = 12.3. (Use a hand calculator for this calculation.) Now let MINITAB do the rest for you. Click on **Calc → Probability Distributions → Normal.** On the input screen, select **Cumulative probability.** Enter 2716 for the **Mean** and 12.3 for the **Standard deviation.** Next select **Input Constant** and enter the value 2750. Click on **OK** and the probability should appear in the Session Window.

Cumulative Distribution Function

```
Normal with mean = 2716.00 and standard deviation = 12.3000

    x      P( X <= x )
  2750        0.9971
```

Since you want to know the probability that the mean calorie intake is greater than 2750, you should subtract this probability from 1. So 1 - .9971 = .0029.

▶ Problem 9 (pg. 435) Serum Cholesterol

HDL cholesterol of females 20-29 years old is normally distributed with $\mu=53$ and $\sigma=13.4$. For parts a through e, click on **Calc** $\rightarrow$ **Probability Distributions** $\rightarrow$ **Normal.** On the input screen, select **Cumulative probability.** Enter 53 for the **Mean.**

(a) Enter 13.4 for the **Standard deviation.** Next select **Input Constant** and enter the value 60. Click on **OK.** To find the probability that HDL is above 60, subtract the probability from 1. $(1 - .6993 = .3007)$

(b) Since you have a sample of n=15, use a hand calculator to calculate the standard deviation, $13.4 / \sqrt{15} = 3.46$. Enter 3.46 for the **Standard deviation.** Next select **Input Constant** and enter the value 60. Click on **OK.** To find the probability that HDL is above 60, subtract the probability from 1. $(1 - .9785 = .0215)$

(c) Since you have a sample of n=20, use a hand calculator to calculate the standard deviation, $13.4 / \sqrt{20} = 3.00$. Enter 3.00 for the **Standard deviation.** Next select **Input Constant** and enter the value 60. Click on **OK.** To find the probability that HDL is above 60, subtract the probability from 1. $(1 - .9902 = .0098)$

▸ Problem 21 (pg. 436)   Simulation

Scores on the Stanford-Binet IQ test are normally distributed with mean 100 and standard deviation 16.

Parts (a), (b), (c), and (e): Approximate the sampling distribution of $\overline{x}$ by taking 500 simple random samples of size n=20. Click on **Calc** → **Random Data** → **Normal. Generate** 500 **rows of data** and **Store in columns** C1-C20. Enter 100 for the **Mean** and 16 for the **Standard deviation**. Click on **OK**. There will be 500 rows and 20 columns of random data in the Minitab worksheet. Each row represents a sample of size n=20. Since this is random data, everyone's data will be different. Next, calculate the mean of each of the samples. Click on **Calc** → **Row Statistics.** Click on **Mean,** select **Input variables** C1-C20 and **Store result in** C21. Click on **OK** and C21 will contain the averages for each row of 20 data points. To draw a histogram of the sample means, click on **Stat** → **Basic Statistics** → **Display Descriptive Statistics.** Select C21 for the **Variable** and click on **Graphs**. Select **Histogram of Data** and click on **OK** twice to view the histogram.

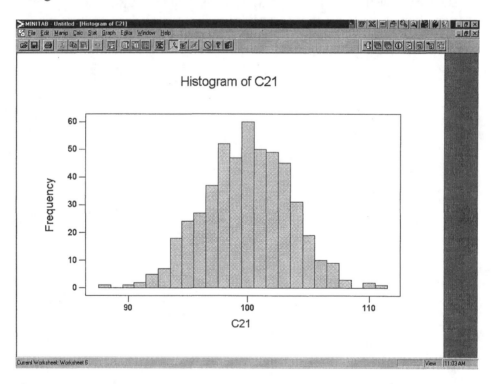

Notice that the histogram is quite symmetric, just like the original normal population. The descriptive statistics of the sample means are in the Session Window and can be seen after the Graph Window is closed.

Descriptive Statistics: C21

Variable	N	Mean	Median	TrMean	StDev	SE Mean
C21	500	99.888	99.950	99.895	3.521	0.157

Variable	Minimum	Maximum	Q1	Q3
C21	88.454	110.808	97.617	102.374

Notice that the mean of the 500 sample means is 99.950 and the standard deviation is 3.521. (Notice how close these are to the theoretical mean and standard deviation of 100 and 3.58.)

Part (f): click on **Calc → Probability Distributions → Normal.** On the input screen, select **Cumulative probability.** Enter 100 for the **Mean.** Since you have a sample of n=20, use a hand calculator to calculate the standard deviation, $16 / \sqrt{20} = 3.58$. Enter 3.58 for the **Standard deviation.** Next select **Input Constant** and enter the value 108. Click on **OK.** To find the probability that the mean IQ is above 108, subtract the probability from 1. (1 - .9873 = .0127)

Part (g): To find the percent of the 500 random samples that had a sample mean IQ greater than 108, click on **Stat → Tables → Tally.** Select C21 for the **Variable** and click on **OK.** A frequency table will be displayed in the Session Window. Count up the number of data points that are greater than 108. In this example, there are 4. So the percent is 4/500 = .008. Notice that this is just a little smaller than the probability that was calculated in part (f) of this problem.

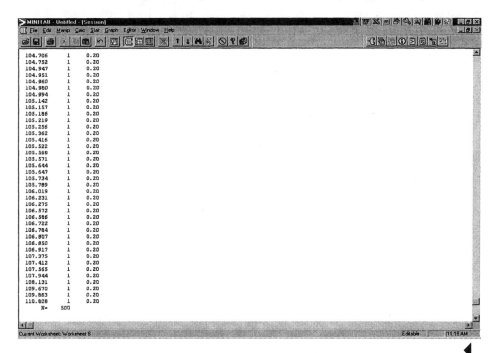

Confidence Intervals

CHAPTER

8

Section 8.1

▶ Example 2 (pg. 459)   Constructing 20 95% Confidence Intervals
Based on 20 Samples

Scores on the Stanford-Binet IQ test are normally distributed with mean 100 and standard deviation 16. Thus, you have a normally distributed population with a <u>known</u> mean and <u>known</u> standard deviation. Simulate 20 simple random samples of size n=15. Click on **Calc → Random Data → Normal. Generate** 15 **rows of data** and **Store in columns** C1-C20. Enter 100 for the **Mean** and 16 for the **Standard deviation**. Click on **OK**. There will be 15 rows and 20 columns of random data in the Minitab worksheet. Each column represents a sample of size n=15 from the normal population with $\mu=100$ and $\sigma=16$. Since this is random data, everyone's data will be different. In this example, we already know that $\mu=100$, so we can actually see how well the confidence intervals do at estimating μ. To construct the confidence intervals, click on **Stat→ Basic Statistics → 1-Sample Z.** Select C1-C20 for the **Variable**. For **Sigma,** enter 16.

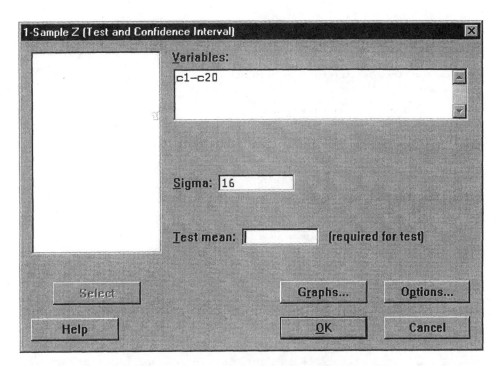

Next, click on **Options** and enter 95.0 for the **Confidence Level.**

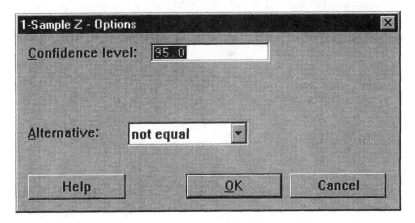

Click on **OK** twice and the results will be displayed in the Session Window.

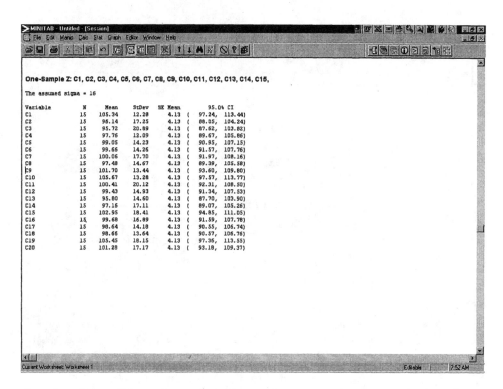

Examine the confidence intervals and count how many do not contain 100, the true population mean. In these samples (above), notice that all of them contain 100.

▶ Example 3 (pg. 462) Construct a 90% confidence interval

Enter the data from Table 1 on page 457 into C1. First verify that the data is
approximately normal. To draw a normal probability plot, click on **Graph** →
Probability Plot. Select C1 for the **Variable** and be sure that the **Distribution** is
Normal.

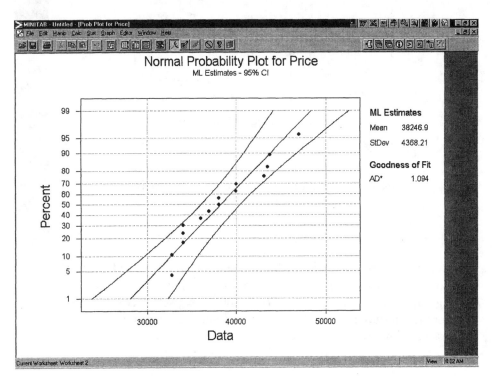

All data points are contained within the bounds of the plot. Next, check for
outliers using a boxplot. Click on **Graph** → **Boxplot.** Select C1 for the
Variable. Click on **Options** and select **Transpose X and Y.** Click on **OK**.

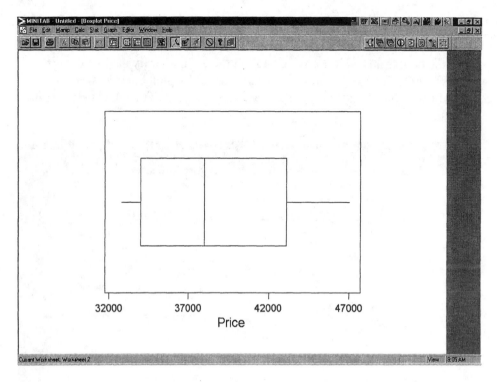

There are no outliers shown in the boxplot, so construct the confidence interval.
Click on **Stat → Basic Statistics → 1-Sample Z.** Select C1 for the **Variable**.
For **Sigma,** enter the assumed value of $4100. Next, select **Options** and enter
90.0 for the **Confidence Level.** Click on **OK** and the interval will be displayed in
the Session Window.

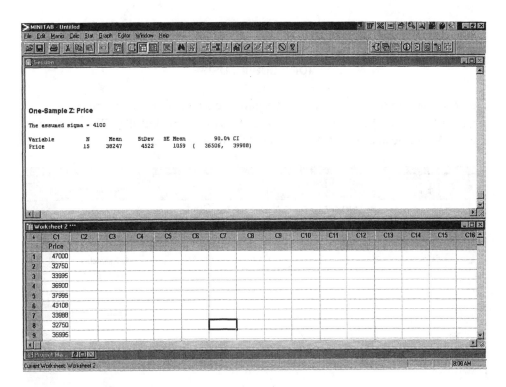

So, the confidence interval is ($36506, $39988).

▶ Problem 15 (pg. 468) Construct 90 and 95% confidence intervals
for Repair Costs

Enter the data into C1. To find the mean of the data and draw a normal
probability plot at the same time, click on **Graph** → **Probability Plot.** Select C1
for the **Variable** and be sure that the **Distribution** is Normal.

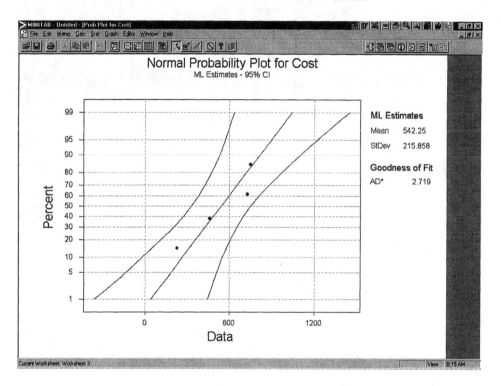

Notice that the mean of the data is listed on the plot, $542.25. The data points
are within the bounds of the normal plot. Next, check for outliers using a boxplot.
Click on **Graph** → **Boxplot.** Select C1 for the **Variable.** Click on **Options** and
select **Transpose X and Y.** Click on **OK.**

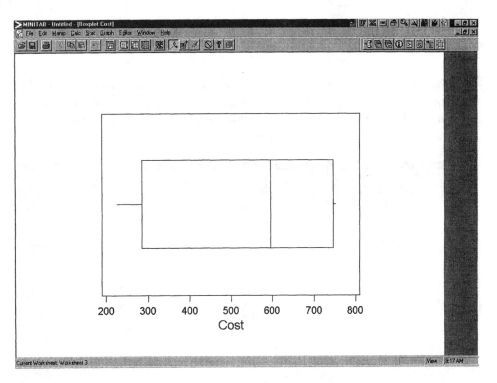

There are no outliers shown in the boxplot, so construct the confidence interval.
Click on **Stat → Basic Statistics → 1-Sample Z.** Select C1 for the **Variable.**
For **Sigma,** enter the assumed value of $220. Next, select **Options** and enter
95.0 for the **Confidence Level.** Click on **OK** and the interval will be displayed in
the Session Window. Repeat this last step to find a 90% confidence interval also.

One-Sample Z: Cost

The assumed sigma = 220

Variable	N	Mean	StDev	SE Mean		95.0% CI
Cost	4	542	249	110	(	327,758)

One-Sample Z: Cost

The assumed sigma = 220

Variable	N	Mean	StDev	SE Mean		90.0% CI
Cost	4	542	249	110	(	361,723)

▶ Problem 19 (pg. 470)   Construct a 92% confidence interval
                          for ACT Math Scores

Open Minitab worksheet **8_1_19**. The scores are in C1. To find the mean of the
data and draw a normal probability plot at the same time, click on **Graph**→
Probability Plot. Select C1 for the **Variable** and be sure that the **Distribution** is
Normal.

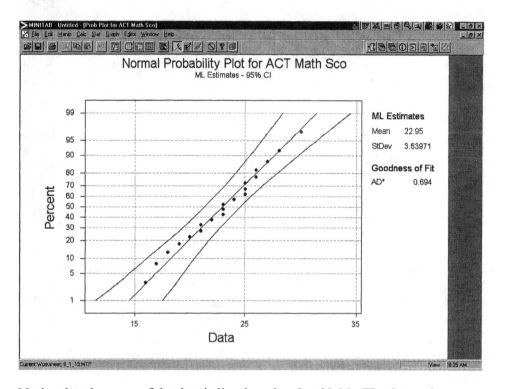

Notice that the mean of the data is listed on the plot, 22.95. The data points are
within the bounds of the normal plot. Next, check for outliers using a boxplot.
Click on **Graph** → **Boxplot.** Select C1 for the **Variable.** Click on **Options** and
select **Transpose X and Y.** Click on **OK**.

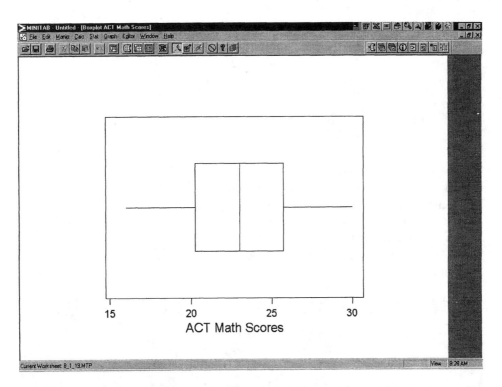

There are no outliers shown in the boxplot, so construct the confidence interval. Click on **Stat → Basic Statistics → 1-Sample Z.** Select C1 for the **Variable.** For **Sigma,** enter the assumed value of 5. Next, select **Options** and enter 92.0 for the **Confidence Level.** Click on **OK** and the interval will be displayed in the Session Window.

One-Sample Z: ACT Math Scores

```
The assumed sigma = 5

Variable          N      Mean     StDev   SE Mean        92.0% CI
ACT Math Sco     20     22.95      3.73      1.12    (20.99,24.91)
```

Notice that the confidence interval for this class data is *above* the population mean score of 20.77. This indicates that this class scored better than the general population.

Section 8.2

▶ Example 1 (pg. 478) Finding t-values

Find the t-value such that the area under the t-distribution to right of the t-value is 0.10, assuming 15 degrees of freedom. Click on **Calc → Probability Distributions → t.** Select **Inverse cumulative probability** with a **Noncentrality parameter** of 0. Enter 15 **Degrees of freedom.** Recall that cumulative probability is calculated as the area to the left of a value. Since the area to the *right* of the t-value is 0.10, the area to the *left* of the t-value is 0.90. Select **Input constant** and enter .90. Click on **OK** and the t-value will be in the Session window.

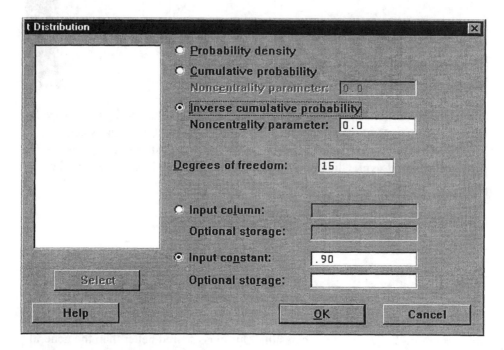

Inverse Cumulative Distribution Function

```
Student's t distribution with 15 DF

P( X <= x )          x
   0.9000        1.3406
```

As you can see, the t-value is 1.3406.

▶ Example 2 (pg. 480) Construct a 90% Confidence Interval for the mean price of a used Corvette

Enter the data from Table 5 on page 480 into C1. First verify that the data is approximately normal. To draw a normal probability plot, click on **Graph** → **Probability Plot.** Select C1 for the **Variable** and be sure that the **Distribution** is Normal. All data points are contained within the bounds of the plot. Next, check for outliers using a boxplot. Click on **Graph** → **Boxplot.** Select C1 for the **Variable.** Click on **Options** and select **Transpose X and Y.** Click on **OK.** (Both of these plots are shown in Example 3 in section 8.1) Since n=15 and the population standard deviation is unknown, you should construct a t-interval for this problem. Click on **Stat** → **Basic Statistics** → **1-Sample t.** Select C1 for the **Variable.** Next, select **Options** and enter 90.0 for the **Confidence Level.** Click on **OK** twice and the output will be displayed in the Session Window.

One-Sample T: C1

Variable	N	Mean	StDev	SE Mean	90.0% CI
C1	15	38247	4522	1167	(36191,40303)

Notice that the confidence interval is ($36191, $40303).

◀

▶ Problem 1 (pg. 484) Finding t-values

For parts (a) - (d), click on **Calc → Probability Distributions → t.** Select **Inverse cumulative probability** with a **Noncentrality parameter** of 0. Then enter the appropriate **Degrees of freedom** and **Input constant**.

Part (a): Find the t-value such that the area under the t-distribution to right of the t-value is 0.10, assuming 25 degrees of freedom. Enter 25 **Degrees of freedom.** Since the area to the *right* of the t-value is 0.10, the area to the *left* of the t-value is 0.90. Select **Input constant** and enter .90. Click on **OK** and the t-value will be in the Session window.

Part (b): Find the t-value such that the area under the t-distribution to right of the t-value is 0.05, assuming 30 degrees of freedom. Enter 30 **Degrees of freedom.** Since the area to the *right* of the t-value is 0.05, the area to the *left* of the t-value is 0.90. Select **Input constant** and enter .95. Click on **OK** and the t-value will be in the Session window.

Part (c): Find the t-value such that the area under the t-distribution to left of the t-value is 0.01, assuming 18 degrees of freedom. Enter 18 **Degrees of freedom.** Select **Input constant** and enter .01. Click on **OK** and the t-value will be in the Session window.

Part (d): Find the critical t-value that corresponds to a 90% confidence level, assuming 20 degrees of freedom. Enter 20 **Degrees of freedom.** Since the center area between the t-values is 0.90, then the area to the *right* of the positive t-value is 0.05, and the area to the *left* of the t-value is 0.95. Select **Input constant** and enter .95. Click on **OK** and the t-value will be in the Session window.

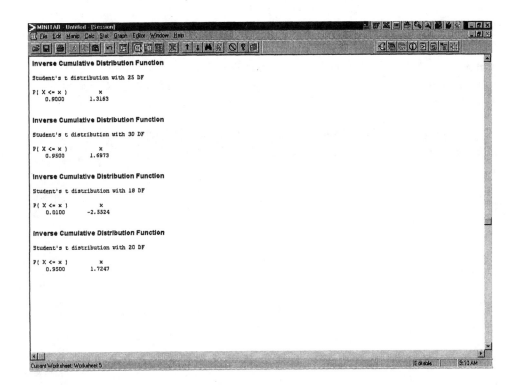

> ▶ Problem 26 (pg. 489)   The Effect of Outliers

Enter the ages into C1. First construct a boxplot of the data to identify any
outliers. Click on **Graph → Boxplot.** Select C1 for the **Variable.** Click on
Options and select **Transpose X and Y.** Click on **OK.**

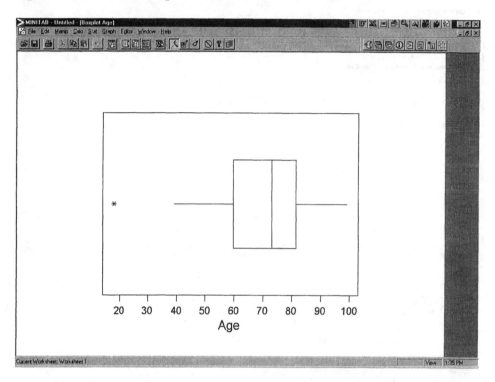

 There is one outlier -- the person who died at age 18. Construct 90% confidence
intervals, with and without the outlier. Since n=14 and the population standard
deviation is unknown, you should construct a t-interval for this problem. Click
on **Stat → Basic Statistics → 1-Sample t.** Select C1 for the **Variable.** Next,
select **Options** and enter 90.0 for the **Confidence Level.** Click on **OK** twice and
the output will be displayed in the Session Window.

One-Sample T: Age

Variable	N	Mean	StDev	SE Mean	90.0% CI
Age	14	68.93	20.73	5.54	(59.12, 78.74)

To construct the interval without the outlier, just delete age=18 from C1 and
repeat the steps above. This time n=13.

One-Sample T: Age

```
Variable          N      Mean     StDev   SE Mean           90.0% CI
Age              13     72.85     15.26      4.23   ( 65.30, 80.39)
```

Notice the difference between the two intervals. The first one, which included the outlier, is wider -- (59.12, 78.74). Compare that to the second interval, which did not include the outlier -- (65.30, 80.39).

◀

Section 8.3

▶ Example 2 (pg. 492) Construct a 95% confidence interval for p

You know that 96 of 1068 American adults said that they had been shot at. To construct a 95% confidence interval, click on **Stat→ Basic Statistics → 1 Proportion.** Select **Summarized Data.** The **Number of trials** is 1068 and the **Number of successes** is 96.

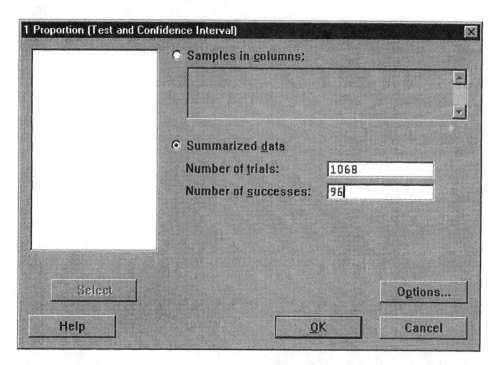

Next, to select the confidence level, click on **Options.** Enter 95.0 for the **Confidence Level.** Also, select **Use test and interval based on normal distribution.**

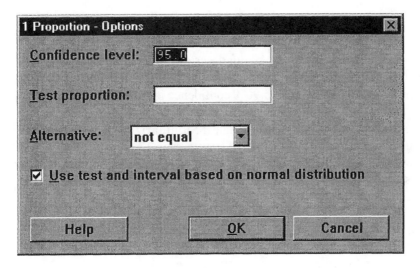

Click on **OK** twice and the output will be displayed in the Session Window.

Test and CI for One Proportion

```
Test of p = 0.5 vs p not = 0.5

Sample  X     N   Sample p       95.0% CI        Z-Value  P-Value
1       96  1068  0.089888  (0.072734, 0.107041)  -26.81    .000
```

Notice the interval is (.073, .107).

▶ Problem 7 (pg. 495) Lipitor

A study of 863 patients who received 10 mg doses of Lipitor found that 47 reported headache as a side effect. Use a hand calculator to verify that $(863)*(.054)*(.946) \geq 10$. Construct a 90% confidence interval for the true proportion of patients who reported headache as a side effect of Lipitor. Click on Stat → Basic Statistics → 1 Proportion. Select Summarized Data. The Number of trials is 863 and the Number of successes is 47. Next, to select the confidence level, click on Options. Enter 90.0 for the Confidence Level. Also, select Use test and interval based on normal distribution. Click on OK twice and the results will be in the Session Window.

Test and CI for One Proportion

```
Test of p = 0.5 vs p not = 0.5

Sample  X     N  Sample p      90.0% CI          Z-Value  P-Value
1      47   863  0.054461  (0.041755, 0.067167)   -26.18    0.000
```

Notice that the sample proportion is displayed (.054461) as well as the confidence interval (.042, .067).

Section 8.4

> ▶ **Example 1 (pg. 500)** Finding Critical Values for the Chi-Square

Find the critical values that separate the middle 90% of the chi-square distribution from the 5% area in each tail, assuming 15 degrees of freedom. Click on **Calc → Probability Distributions →Chi-square.** Select **Inverse cumulative probability** with a **Noncentrality parameter** of 0. Enter 25 **Degrees of freedom.** This will have to be done in two steps. Since the center area between the chi-square values is 0.90, the area in both the upper and lower tail will be 5%. First find the upper chi-square value. The area to the *right* of the upper chi-square value is 0.05, so the area to the *left* of it is 0.95. Select **Input constant** and enter .95. Click on **OK** and the chi-square value will be in the Session window. Now find the lower chi-square value. The area to the *left* of the lower chi-square value is 0.05. Repeat the steps above, but this time select **Input constant** and enter .05.

Inverse Cumulative Distribution Function

```
Chi-Square with 15 DF

P( X <= x )           x
    0.9500       24.9958
```

Inverse Cumulative Distribution Function

```
Chi-Square with 15 DF

P( X <= x )           x
    0.0500        7.2609
```

As you can see, the lower chi-square value is 7.2609 and the upper chi-square value is 24.9958.

▶ Example 2 (pg. 502) Constructing Confidence Intervals for s

Use the prices for the Corvettes (Table 7 on page 502) to construct a 90%
confidence interval about the population standard deviation. In section 8.1, we
verified that this data is normally distributed with a normal probability plot and
verified that there were no outliers with a boxplot. To calculate a 90%
confidence for σ, click on **Stat** → **Basic Statistics** →**Display Descriptive
Statistics.** Select C1 as the **Variable** and click on **Graphs.** Select **Graphical
summary** and enter 90 for the **Confidence level.** Click on **OK** twice.

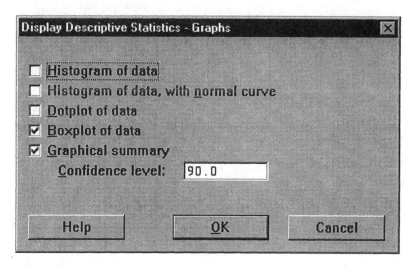

Both a boxplot and a Descriptive Statistics window will be displayed. The
confidence interval for the standard deviation is in the Descriptive Statistics
window.

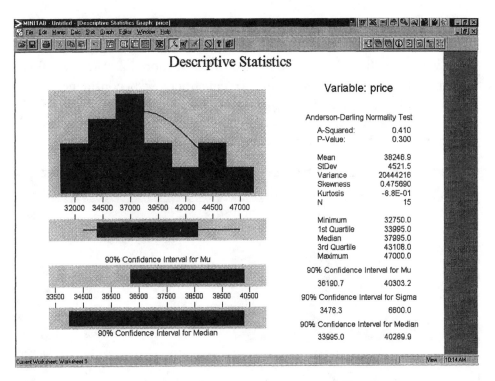

Notice on the right side of the window, near the bottom, the 90% Confidence
Interval for Sigma is (3476.3, 6600.0).

▶ Problem 7 (pg. 51) Wheat Pennies

Open worksheet **8_2_13.** In Problem 13 from Section 8.2, it was verified
that this data is normally distributed. To construct a 95% confidence for σ,
click on **Stat → Basic Statistics →Display Descriptive Statistics.** Select
C1 as the **Variable** and click on **Graphs.** Select **Graphical summary**
and enter 95 for the **Confidence level.** Click on **OK** twice.

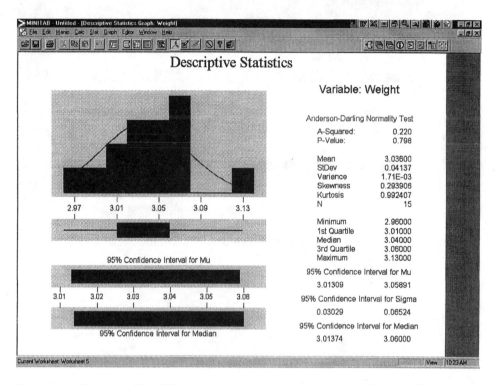

Notice on the right side of the window, near the bottom, the 90% Confidence
Interval for Sigma is (0.03029, 0.06524).

Hypothesis Testing

Section 9.2

▶ Examples 2 & 4 (pg. 533 & 536) Hypothesis Testing

The mean "blue book" price for a 3-year-old Corvette is \$37,500. Grant does not
think that this is true in his neighborhood, so he randomly selects 15
neighborhood on-line dealers and obtains the data found in Table 2 on page 533.
Is there enough evidence to support his claim at $\alpha = .10$? Assume $\sigma=\$4100$. Use
both the classical method and the P-value to interpret.

Enter the data from Table 2 on page 533 of the text into C1 of a Minitab
worksheet. Click on **Stat → Basic Statistics → 1-Sample Z.** Enter C1 for the
Variable, and beside **Sigma,** enter 4100. Click on **Test mean** and enter 37500.

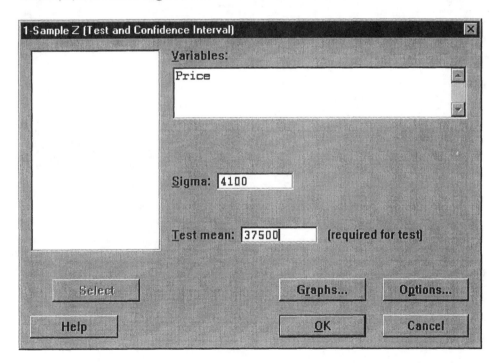

Since the claim is "the mean is different from $37,500", you will perform a two-tailed test. Click on **Options**, and set **Alternative** to "not equal".

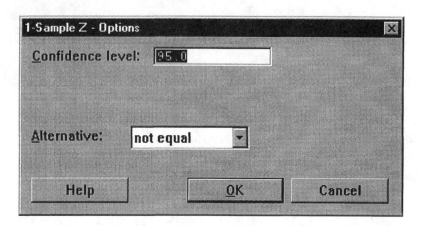

Click on **OK** twice and the results should be displayed in the Session Window.

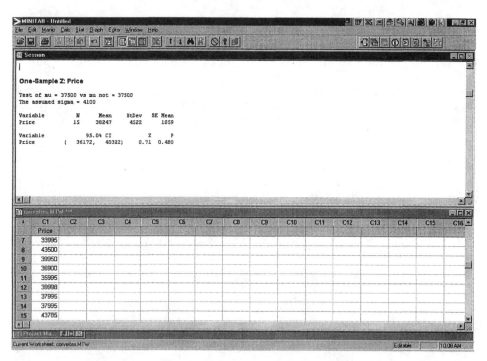

Notice that both the test statistic and the P-value are given. From the output, note that $Z = 0.71$ and $P = .48$. Since Z is less than 1.645 and since the P-value is larger than α, you should Fail to Reject the null hypothesis.

▶ Problem 13 (pg. 540) Acid Rain

A biologist claims that the pH level of the rain in Pierce County, Washington has decreased since 1990. She obtains a random sample of 19 rain dates in the year 2000. Open worksheet **9_2_13.** The rain acidity for the 19 days is in C1. Because n=19, you must verify that pH level is normally distributed and does not contain any outliers. Use a normal probability plot and a boxplot. To draw a normal probability plot, click on **Graph → Probability Plot.** Select C1 for the **Variable** and be sure that the **Distribution** is Normal. All data points are contained within the bounds of the plot.

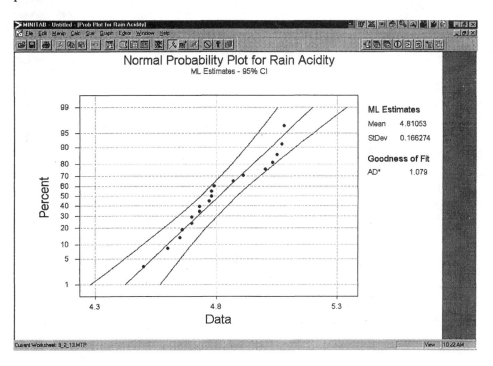

Next, check for outliers using a boxplot. Click on **Graph → Boxplot.** Select C1 for the **Variable.** Click on **Options** and select **Transpose X and Y.** Click on **OK**.

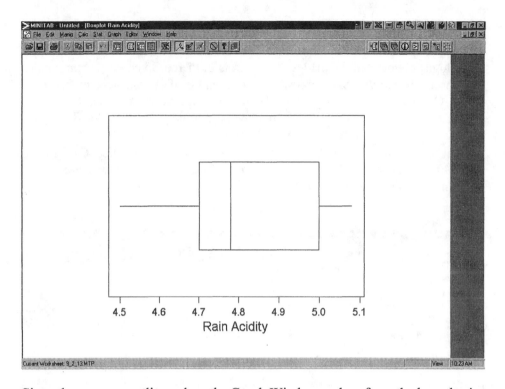

Since there are no outliers, close the Graph Window and perform the hypothesis test. Click on **Stat → Basic Statistics → 1-Sample Z.** Enter C1 for the **Variable,** click on **Test mean** and enter 5.03. Beside **Sigma**, enter the assumed value σ=0.2. Since the claim is "the rain acidity has decreased", you will perform a lower-tailed test. Click on **Options** and use the down arrow beside **Alternative** to select "less than". Click on **OK** and the results of the test should be displayed in the Session Window.

One-Sample Z: Rain Acidity

```
Test of mu = 5.03 vs mu < 5.03
The assumed sigma = 0.2

Variable          N        Mean      StDev    SE Mean
Rain Acidity     19      4.8105     0.1708     0.0459

Variable     95.0% Upper Bound          Z       P
Rain Acidity             4.8860      -4.78   0.000
```

Since P=0.00, reject the null hypothesis at any significance level. Therefore, the biologist is correct in thinking that the pH level of rain has decreased since 1990.

> **Problem 15 (pg. 542)** Filling Bottles

A quality control manager wishes to verify that the mean amount of juice in each bottle is 64 ounces. She obtains a random sample of 22 bottles and measures the content. Open worksheet **9_2_15.** The ounces of juice are in C1. Because n=22, we must verify that pH level is normally distributed and does not contain any outliers. Use a normal probability plot and a boxplot. To draw a normal probability plot, click on **Graph → Probability Plot.** Select C1 for the **Variable** and be sure that the **Distribution** is Normal. All data points are contained within the bounds of the plot. Next, check for outliers using a boxplot. Click on **Graph → Boxplot.** Select C1 for the **Variable.** Click on **Options** and select **Transpose X and Y.** Click on **OK.** Since there are no outliers, proceed to perform the hypothesis test. Click on **Stat → Basic Statistics → 1-Sample Z.** Enter C1 for the **Variable,** click on **Test mean** and enter 64. Beside **Sigma,** enter the assumed value σ=0.06. Since the manager is interested in whether or not the bottles contain 64 oz., you will perform a two-tailed test. Click on **Options** and use the down arrow beside **Alternative** to select "not equal". Click on **OK** and the results of the test should be displayed in the Session Window.

One-Sample Z: Apple Juice (oz)

```
Test of mu = 64 vs mu not = 64
The assumed sigma = 0.06

Variable          N      Mean    StDev   SE Mean
Apple Juice      22   63.9577   0.0503    0.0128

Variable             95.0% CI           Z      P
Apple Juice    ( 63.9327, 63.9828)   -3.30  0.001
```

Since P = .001 and is less than α, you should Reject the null hypothesis. Since you are rejecting the null hypothesis, the data provides evidence that the average amount of juice in the bottles is NOT 64 ounces, therefore the assembly line should be shut down so that the filling machine can be recalibrated.

Section 9.3

> ▶ Example 1 (pg. 548) Testing μ with a Small Sample, σ Unknown

A nutritionist claims that the mean daily caffeine intake of 20-29-year-old females has increased since 1996 when it was reported to be 142.8 mg. She takes a random sample of 20 females in this age group. At $\alpha = .05$, is there enough evidence to support her claim?

Enter the data into C1. (The data can be found in Table 3 on page 548 of the textbook.) Since this is a small sample problem, you will be performing a 1-Sample t-test, but first verify that the data is approximately normal and has no outliers. (To draw a normal probability plot, click on **Graph → Probability Plot.** Select C1 for the **Variable** and be sure that the **Distribution** is Normal. All data points are contained within the bounds of the plot. Next, check for outliers using a boxplot. Click on **Graph → Boxplot.** Select C1 for the **Variable.** Click on **Options** and select **Transpose X and Y.** Click on **OK.**) Since there are no outliers, proceed to perform the hypothesis test. For this type of problem, MINITAB calculates the sample standard deviation automatically. Click on **Stat → Basic Statistics → 1-Sample t.** Enter C1 for the **Variable,** click on **Test mean** and enter 142.8. Since it is suspected that the caffeine intake has increased, you will perform an upper-tailed test. Click on **Options** and then on the down arrow beside **Alternative** to select "greater than". Click on **OK** and the results of the test should be displayed in the Session Window.

One-Sample T: caffeine

```
Test of mu = 142.8 vs mu > 142.8

Variable          N      Mean     StDev   SE Mean
caffeine         20    147.47     22.26      4.98

Variable     95.0% Lower Bound        T      P
caffeine                 138.86     0.94  0.180
```

Notice that MINITAB gives the test statistic and the P-value, so that you can make your conclusion using either value. Since the P-value is larger than α, you would Fail to Reject the null hypothesis. There is not enough evidence to support the nutritionist's claim that the mean caffeine intake has increased since 1996.

> Problem 27 (pg. 557) Temperature of Surgical Patients

Open Minitab worksheet 9_3_27. Click on **Stat→ Basic Statistics →1-Sample t.** Enter C1 for the **Variable,** click on **Test mean** and enter 98.2. Since the claim is that the mean temperature of surgical patients is above the normal temperature, you will perform an upper-tailed test. Click on **Options** and then on the down arrow beside **Alternative** to select "greater than". Click on **OK** twice and the results of the test should be displayed in the Session Window.

One-Sample T: Patient Temperature

```
Test of mu = 98.2 vs mu > 98.2

Variable          N      Mean    StDev   SE Mean
Patient Temp     32    98.291    0.689     0.122

Variable      95.0% Lower Bound        T      P
Patient Temp            98.084      0.74  0.231
```

Since the P-value is .231 and is greater than α, you do not reject the null hypothesis. There is not enough evidence that surgical patients have a higher mean temperature than normal.

◀

▶ Problem 29 (pg. 557) Simulation

Create 40 random samples of size n=20. Click on **Calc**→ **Random data** →
Normal. Generate 20 **rows of data** and **Store in columns** C1-C40. Enter a
Mean of 50 and a **Standard deviation** of 10. Click on **OK**. Each column
contains a random sample of size n=20.

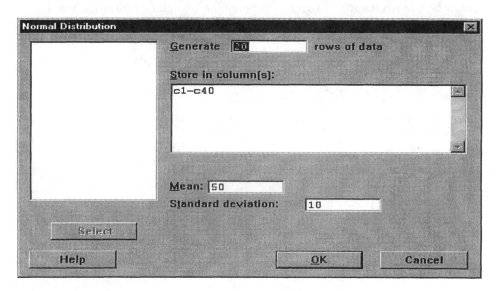

Now, perform t-tests on each column. Click on **Stat**→ **Basic Statistics** →**1-
Sample t.** Enter C1-C40 for the **Variable,** click on **Test mean** and enter 50.
Click on **Options** and then on the down arrow beside **Alternative** to select "not
equal". Click on **OK** and the results of the 40 tests should be displayed in the
Session Window.   To count the number of samples that would lead to a rejection
of the null hypothesis, simply count the number of times that the P-value is less
than .05. Divide this number by 40 for the result.

Section 9.4

▶ Example 1 (pg. 560) Hypothesis Test for a Proportion

In 1995, 74% of Americans felt that men were more aggressive than women. A poll was conducted in 2000. Of 1026 Americans, 698 felt men were more aggressive than women. At $\alpha = .05$, is there enough evidence to indicate that the percentage of Americans who believe this has decreased since 1995? Use a hand-calculator to verify that the assumptions required to perform the hypothesis test are met. Since they are, click on **Stat** → **Basic Statistics** → **1-Proportion.** The data is given in a summarized form, so select **Summarized data**. Enter 1026 for the **Number of trials.** The **Number of Successes** is 698.

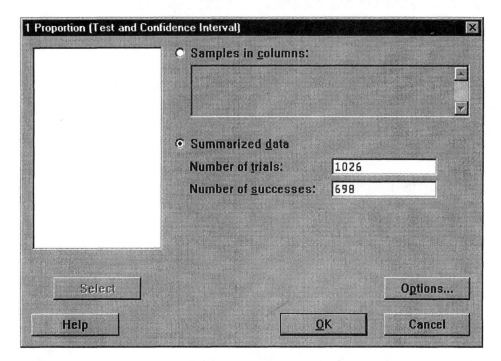

Click on **Options**. Enter .74 for the **Test Proportion** because in 1995, 74% believed that men are more aggressive than women, and select "less than" for the **Alternative**. Since you verified that the requirements were met for this problem, click on **Use test and interval based on normal distribution,** and then click on **OK** twice.

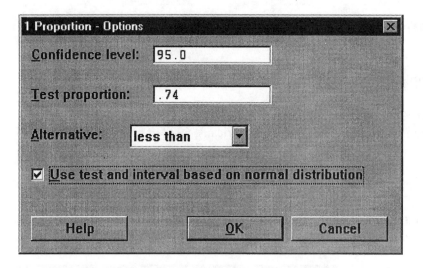

The results should be displayed in the Session Window.

Test and CI for One Proportion

```
Test of p = 0.74 vs p < 0.74

Sample      X      N  Sample p  95.0% Upper Bound  Z-Value  P-Value
1         698   1026  0.680312           0.704260    -4.36    0.000
```

Notice that the test statistic (z = -4.36), the P-value (P = .000) and a 95%
confidence interval for the true proportion of Americans holding this belief are
all displayed in the output. With such a small P-value, you should Reject the null
hypothesis. Thus, the proportion of Americans who believe that men are more
aggressive than women has decreased since 1995.

▸ Example 3 (pg. 564) Hypothesis test for Population Proportion

Test whether an advertising campaign increased the proportion of males who consume the minimum daily requirement of calcium from 48.9. A random sample of n=35 males after the campaign found that 21 consumed the RDA of calcium. Use a hand-calculator to verify that the assumption of normality is met. Minitab easily handles the situation when the assumptions are NOT met. Click on **Stat → Basic Statistics → 1-Proportion.** The data is given in a summarized form, so select **Summarized data.** Enter 35 for the **Number of trials.** The **Number of Successes** is 21. Click on **Options.** Enter .489 for the **Test Proportion** because it is was known that before the ad campaign, 48.9% consumed the RDA of calcium, and select "greater than" for the **Alternative.** Be sure that you do **NOT** select **Use test and interval based on normal distribution,** and then click on **OK** twice.

Test and CI for One Proportion

```
Test of p = 0.489 vs p > 0.489

                                               Exact
Sample     X      N  Sample p  95.0% Lower Bound  P-Value
1         21     35  0.600000          0.447176    0.126
```

Since the P-value is .126 and is larger than α = .10, you do not reject the null hypothesis. Thus, there is not enough evidence to prove that the advertising campaign was successful in increasing the daily intake of calcium among males in this age group.

◀

> ▶ Problem 7 (pg. 565) Gun Control

Use a hand-calculator to verify that the requirements of the test are met. Since
they are, click on **Stat → Basic Statistics → 1-Proportion.** The data is given in
a summarized form, so select **Summarized data**. Enter 1012 for the **Number of
trials** and the **Number of Successes** is 395. Click on **Options**. Enter .47 for the
Test Proportion because in 1990 47% had a gun, and select "less than" for the
Alternative. Click on **Use test and interval based on normal distribution,** and
then click on **OK** twice.

Test and CI for One Proportion

```
Test of p = 0.47 vs p < 0.47

Sample     X      N  Sample p  95.0% Upper Bound  Z-Value  P-Value
1        395   1012  0.390316           0.415539    -5.08    0.000
```

Since the P-value is so small you would reject the null hypothesis. There is
evidence to show that the proportion of households that have a gun has decreased
since 1990.

◀

▶ Problem 23 (pg. 567) Small Sample Hypothesis Test

Use a hand-calculator to verify that the requirements of the test are met. Since $120*.025*.975 < 10$, they are not met. Click on **Stat → Basic Statistics → 1-Proportion.** The data is given in a summarized form, so select **Summarized data**. Enter 120 for the **Number of trials** and the **Number of Successes** is 3. Click on **Options**. Enter .04 for the **Test Proportion** because in 1997 4% of mothers smoked more than 21 cigarettes during pregnancy, and select "less than" for the **Alternative**. Be sure **NOT** to select **Use test and interval based on normal distribution,** and then click on **OK** twice.

Test and CI for One Proportion

```
Test of p = 0.04 vs p < 0.04

                                              Exact
Sample      X      N  Sample p  95.0% Upper Bound  P-Value
1           3    120  0.025000           0.063344    0.289
```

Since the P-value is .289, which is larger than $\alpha = .05$, you do not reject the null hypothesis. Thus, there is not enough evidence to prove that the proportion of pregnant mothers who smoke more than 21 cigarettes has decreased since 1997.

◀

Section 9.5

▶ Example 3 (pg. 572)   Finding P-values for a Chi-Square Test

Once you have calculated the test statistic, χ^2, MINITAB can calculate the exact P-value of the test for you. In Example 1 on page 570 of the text, $\chi^2 = 25.996$ and there are 19 degrees of freedom. Click on **Calc → Probability distributions → Chi-square.** Select **Cumulative Probability** and enter 19 **Degrees of Freedom.** Next, click on **Input Constant** and enter the test statistic, 25.996. Click on **OK** and the output will be displayed in the Session Window.
Cumulative Distribution Function

```
Chi-Square with 19 DF

          x       P( X <= x )
    25.9960         0.8697
```

Since you have found $P(\chi^2 < 25.996) = .8697$, you need to subtract the probability from 1 to find the P-value. So, the P-value is $1 - .8697 = .1303$. Since this P-value is larger than $\alpha = .10$, you do not reject the null hypothesis.

▸ Problem 9 (pg. 574) Acid Rain

Calculate the test statistic: $\chi^2 = (19-1)*(.1708^2)/(.2^2) = 13.128$. Once you have calculated the test statistic, χ^2, MINITAB can calculate the exact P-value of the test for you. $\chi^2 = 13.128$ and there are 18 degrees of freedom. Click on **Calc → Probability distributions → Chi-square.** Select **Cumulative Probability** and enter 18 **Degrees of Freedom.** Next, click on **Input Constant** and enter the test statistic, 13.128. Click on **OK** and the output will be displayed in the Session Window.

Cumulative Distribution Function

```
Chi-Square with 18 DF

          x      P( X <= x )
    13.1280          0.2161
```

Since you have found P-value = .2161, which is larger than $\alpha = .05$, you do not reject the null hypothesis that $\sigma=.2$.

◀

Inferences on Two Samples

CHAPTER

10

Section 10.1

> Example 2 (pg. 596) Matched Pairs Data

Enter the data, found in Table 1 on page 597 of the textbook, into the MINITAB Data Worksheet. Put the Dominant Hand data in C1 and the Non-dominant Hand data in C2. First calculate a set of differences and check that they are approximately normal and there are no outliers. Click on **Calc→ Calculator.** **Store result in** C3 and enter C1 - C2 for the **Expression.** To draw a normal probability plot, click on **Graph→ Probability Plot.** Select C3 for the **Variable** and be sure that the **Distribution** is Normal. All data points are contained within the bounds of the plot. Next, check for outliers using a boxplot. Click on **Graph → Boxplot.** Select C3 for the **Variable.** Click on **Options** and select **Transpose X and Y.** Click on **OK**. Since there are no outliers, proceed to perform the hypothesis test. Click on **Stat→ Basic Statistics → Paired t.** Enter C1 for the **First Sample** and C2 for the **Second Sample.**

Paired t (Test and Confidence Interval)	☒

C1	Dominant	**First sample:**	Dominant
C2	Non-dominar	**Second sample:**	'Non-dominant'

Paired t evaluates the first sample minus the second sample.

Select	Graphs...	Options...
Help	OK	Cancel

Click on **Options.** Enter 0 for **Test Mean** and select **less than** as the
Alternative.

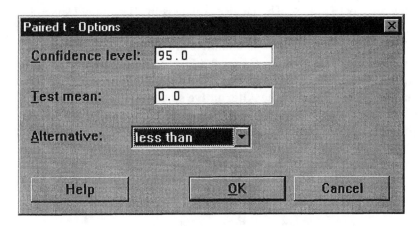

Click on **OK** twice to display the results in the Session Window.

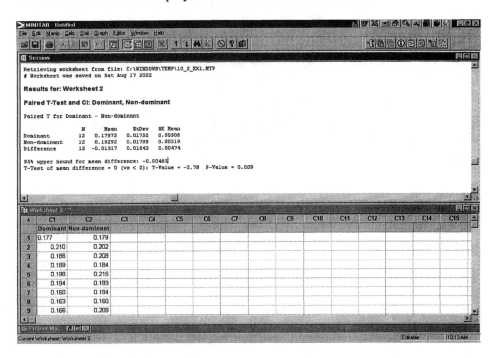

Notice that both the test statistic, t = -2.78, and the P-value = .009 are given.
With such a small p-value, you Reject the null hypothesis. There is evidence to
support Professor Neil's claim.
**Note: Since you performed a left-tailed test, only the upper bound for the
confidence interval is shown. To calculate a confidence interval, you must
choose "not equal" as the alternative hypothesis.**

▶ Problem 9 (pg. 602) Muzzle Velocity

Open Minitab worksheet **10_1_9**. The Device A data is in C1 and the Device B data is in C2. Notice that for both samples, n = 12. The problem tells you that the differences are approximately normal and there are no outliers. Click on **Stat** → **Basic Statistics** → **Paired t.** Enter C1 for the **First Sample** and C2 for the **Second Sample.** Click on **Options.** Enter 99 for **Confidence level**, enter 0 for **Test Mean** and select **not equal** as the **Alternative** since you are testing if there is a difference in the measurements of Device A and B. Click on **OK** twice and the results of the test should be displayed in the Session Window.

Paired T-Test and CI: A, B

```
Paired T for A - B

               N      Mean    StDev    SE Mean
A             12   792.458    1.407     0.406
B             12   792.342    1.603     0.463
Difference    12     0.117    0.475     0.137

99% CI for mean difference: (-0.309, 0.542)
T-Test of mean difference = 0 (vs not = 0): T-Value = 0.85  P-
Value = 0.413
```

Notice that the test statistic is T = .85 with a P-value = .413. Since this P-value is so large, you would Fail to Reject H_0 at any α level. Thus, there is not enough evidence to prove that Device A and B are any different. The 99% confidence interval is (-0.309, .542).

▶ Problem 13 (pg. 603)   Seechi Disk

Open Minitab worksheet **10_1_13**. The Initial Depth data is in C2 and the Depth 5 years later is in C3. Notice that for both samples, n = 8. The problem tells you that the differences are approximately normal and there are no outliers. Click on **Stat → Basic Statistics → Paired t.** Enter C2 for the **First Sample** and C3 for the **Second Sample.** Click on **Options.** Enter 0 for **Test Mean** and select **less than** as the **Alternative** since if the water is clearer 5 years later, the depth will be a larger number and thus the difference will be less than 0. Click on **OK** twice and the results of the test should be displayed in the Session Window.

Paired T-Test and CI: Initial Depth, Depth 5 years later

```
Paired T for Initial Depth - Depth 5 years later

                N     Mean    StDev   SE Mean
Initial Dept    8    54.38    12.69      4.49
Depth 5 year    8    59.50     8.73      3.09
Difference      8    -5.13     6.08      2.15

95% upper bound for mean difference: -1.05
T-Test of mean difference = 0 (vs < 0): T-Value = -2.38
P-Value = 0.024
```

Notice that the test statistic is T = -2.38 with a P-value = .024. Since this P-value is larger than α=.02, you would Fail to Reject H_0. Thus, there is sufficient evidence to prove that the water is clearer 5 years later. To construct a 95% confidence interval repeat the above steps, choosing **not equal** as the **Alternative** and 95 for the **Confidence level.** The 95% confidence interval for the mean difference is (-10.21, -0.04).

◀

Section 10.2

▶ **Example 1 & 2 (pg. 610 & 613)** Testing a Claim Regarding Two Means

Open Minitab Worksheet **10_2_Ex1.** The Flight measurements are in C1 and the Control group measurements are in C2. First check that the data is approximately normal and there are no outliers. Draw a normal probability plot for each column of data. Click on **Graph** → **Probability Plot.** Select C1 for the **Variable** and be sure that the **Distribution** is Normal. Repeat this for C2. All data points are contained within the bounds of the plot. Next, check for outliers using a boxplot. Click on **Graph** → **Boxplot.** Select C1 and C2 for the **Y-Variable.** Click on **Options** and select **Transpose X and Y.** Click on **Frame** → **Multiple Graphs** and select **Overlay graphs on the same page.** Click on **OK** twice. Since there are no outliers in either boxplot, proceed to perform the hypothesis test. Click on **Stat** → **Basic Statistics** → **2-Sample t.** Select **Samples in different columns** and enter C1 for the **First** and C2 for the **Second** column. Click on **Options**, and then on the down arrow beside **Alternative** and select **not equal** since you want to test whether the mean red blood cell masses are different. Click on **OK** twice and the results of the test should be displayed in the Session Window.

Two-Sample T-Test and CI: Flight, Control

```
Two-sample T for Flight vs Control

           N     Mean    StDev   SE Mean
Flight    14     7.88     1.02    0.27
Control   14     8.43     1.01    0.27

Difference = mu Flight - mu Control
Estimate for difference:  -0.549
95% CI for difference: (-1.337, 0.238)
T-Test of difference = 0 (vs not =): T-Value = -1.44
                                     P-Value = 0.163   DF = 25
```

Notice that the test statistic is T= -1.44. Since the P-value = .163 and is greater than the α-level of .05, there is not enough evidence to conclude that the mean red blood cell masses are different. The 95% confidence interval is also shown. It is (-1.337, 0.238). (Note that Minitab uses 25 degrees of freedom, rather than 13 as is used in the textbook. The p-values and the confidence intervals will be slightly different.)

▶ Problem 9 (pg. 616) Concrete strength

Open Minitab worksheet **10_2_9**. The Mixture 67-0-301 data is in C1 and the Mixture 67-0-400 data is in C2. The problem tells you that normal probability plots indicate that the data is approximately normal, and boxplots show no outliers. First, notice the confidence interval is looking at the difference μ_{400} - μ_{301}. Thus, use C2 as the first and C1 as the second. Click on **Stat → Basic Statistics → 2-Sample t.** Select **Samples in different columns** and enter C2 for the **First** and C1 for the **Second** column. Click on **Options**, and then on the down arrow beside **Alternative** and select **greater than** since you want to test if the 67-0-400 mixture is stronger than the 67-0-301 mixture. Click on **OK** twice and the results of the test should be displayed in the Session Window.

Two-Sample T-Test and CI: Mixture 67-0-400, Mixture 67-0301

```
Two-sample T for Mixture 67-0-400 vs Mixture 67-0301

            N      Mean    StDev   SE Mean
Mixture    10      4483      474       150
Mixture     9      3669      459       153


Difference = mu Mixture 67-0-400 - mu Mixture 67-0301
Estimate for difference:  814
90% lower bound for difference: 528
T-Test of difference = 0 (vs >): T-Value = 3.80   P-Value = 0.001
DF = 16
```

Since the p-value is so small, you would reject the null hypothesis. There is not enough evidence to prove that the 67-0-400 mix is stronger. To find the 90% confidence interval, repeat the steps above, but this time click on **Options**, and select **not equal** as the **Alternative.** Be sure to enter 90 for the **Confidence Level.** Click on **OK** twice and the appropriate confidence interval should be displayed in the Session Window.

Two-Sample T-Test and CI: Mixture 67-0-400, Mixture 67-0301

```
Two-sample T for Mixture 67-0-400 vs Mixture 67-0301

            N      Mean    StDev   SE Mean
Mixture    10      4483      474       150
Mixture     9      3669      459       153


Difference = mu Mixture 67-0-400 - mu Mixture 67-0301
Estimate for difference:  814
90% CI for difference: (440, 1188)
T-Test of difference = 0 (vs not =): T-Value = 3.80   P-Value =
0.002   DF = 16
```

The confidence interval is (440, 1188). This interval is different than the one in the text because of the number of degrees of freedom used by Minitab.

◀

Section 10.3

▶ Example 1 (pg. 622) Testing a claim regarding two proportions

In clinical trials of Nasonex, 3774 patients were randomly divided into an experimental group and a control group. Of the 2103 patients in the experimental group (Group 1), 547 reported headaches as a side effect. Of the 1671 patients in the control group (Group 2), 368 reported headaches as a side effect. This is a summary of the results of the study. First, use a hand calculator to verify the requirements to perform the hypothesis test are met. To test if the proportion of Nasonex users that experienced headaches is greater than the proportion in the control group, click on **Stat → Basic Statistics → 2 Proportions**. Select **Summarized Data** and use the data for Group 1 as the **First sample**. Enter 2103 **Trials** and 547 **Successes**. Use the data for Group 2 as the **Second sample**. Enter 1671 **Trials** and 368 **Successes**.

2 Proportions (Test and Confidence Interval)	☒

○ **Samples in one column:**

Samples: [   ]

Subscripts: [   ]

○ **Samples in different columns:**

First: [   ]

Second: [   ]

⊙ **Summarized data:**

	Trials:	Successes:
First sample:	2103	547
Second sample:	1671	368

[Select]   [Options...]

[Help]   [OK]   [Cancel]

Click on **Options.** Enter 0 for **Test mean**, and select **greater than** as the **Alternative** since you want to test if proportion of Nasonex users that experienced headaches is greater than the proportion in the control group. Next click on **Use pooled estimate of p for test.**

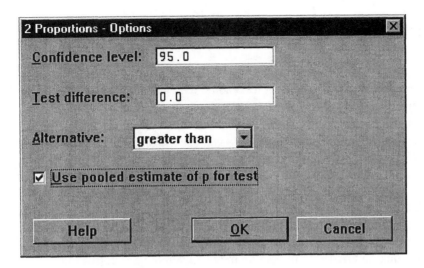

Click on **OK** twice to display the results in the Session Window.

Test and CI for Two Proportions

```
Sample       X       N   Sample p
1          547    2103   0.260105
2          368    1671   0.220227

Estimate for p(1) - p(2):  0.0398772
95% lower bound for p(1) - p(2):  0.0169504
Test for p(1) - p(2) = 0 (vs > 0):   Z = 2.84   P-Value = 0.002
```

Since the P-value is smaller than α, you should Reject the null hypothesis. The evidence suggests that Nasonex users reported more headaches than the control group. **(Note: to construct a confidence interval, the Alternative must be set to "not equal". You can enter any desired confidence level.)**

▶ Problem 11 (pg. 629) Too Much Cholesterol in Your Diet?

Test the claim that a higher proportion of individuals with at most an 8th-grade education than individuals with at least some college consume too much cholesterol. First, use a hand calculator to verify the requirements to perform the hypothesis test are met. Next, click on **Stat → Basic Statistics → 2 Proportions.** Select **Summarized Data** and use the data for individuals with at most an 8th-grade education (Group 1) as the **First sample.** Enter 320 **Trials** and 114 **Successes.** Use the data for individuals with some college (Group 2) as the **Second sample.** Enter 350 **Trials** and 112 **Successes.** Click on **Options.** Enter 0 for **Test mean,** and select **greater than** as the **Alternative** since you want to test if proportion of Group 1 individuals that consume too much cholesterol is greater than the proportion in Group 2. Next click on **Use pooled estimate of p for test.** Click on **OK** twice to display the results in the Session Window.

Test and CI for Two Proportions

```
Sample     X     N   Sample p
1         114   320  0.356250
2         112   350  0.320000


Estimate for p(1) - p(2):  0.03625
95% lower bound for p(1) - p(2):  -0.0239253
Test for p(1) - p(2) = 0 (vs > 0):  Z = 0.99  P-Value = 0.161
```

Since the P-value is larger than α, you should Fail to Reject the null hypothesis. The evidence does NOT suggest that Group 1 consumed more cholesterol than Group 2. To construct a 95% confidence interval, repeat the steps above. This time the **Alternative** must be set to "**not equal**". Enter 95 for the **Confidence level.** Click on **OK** twice to display the results in the Session Window.

Test and CI for Two Proportions

```
Sample     X     N   Sample p
1         114   320  0.356250
2         112   350  0.320000


Estimate for p(1) - p(2):  0.03625
95% CI for p(1) - p(2):  (-0.0354533, 0.107953)
Test for p(1) - p(2) = 0 (vs not = 0):  Z = 0.99  P-Value = 0.322
```

The confidence interval is (-.035, 0.107).

Section 10.4

► Example 2 (pg. 637) Testing a claim regarding two Standard
Deviations

Open worksheet **10_4_EX2.** The data for Cisco Systems is in C1 and the GE
data is in C2. Test the investor's claim that Cisco Systems stock is more volatile
than GE stock. First, verify that both variables are approximately normal with
normal probability plots. Draw a normal probability plot for each column of data.
Click on **Graph → Probability Plot.** Select C1 for the **Variable** and be sure
that the **Distribution** is Normal. Repeat this for C2. All data points are
contained within the bounds of the plots. To perform the test, click on **Stat→
Basic Statistics → 2 Variances.** Select **Samples in different columns** and enter
C1 for the **First** and C2 for the **Second.**

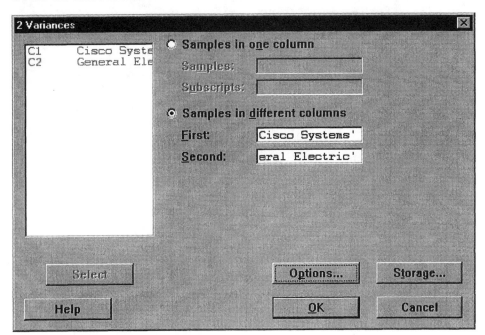

Click on **OK** to display the results in the Session Window.

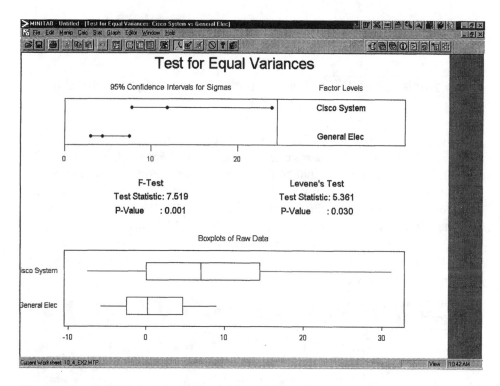

The results of the F-test are shown in the middle of the window. F=7.519 and the p-value is .001. Thus, we would reject the null hypothesis. There is sufficient evidence to show that Cisco Systems stock is more volatile than GE stock.
(Note: Minitab performs the F-test as a two-tailed test. If you want to do a one-tailed test, divide the p-value in half. So, since this problem is an upper-tailed test, the p-value is .0005.)

▶ Problem 19 (pg. 642) Waiting Time in Line

Open worksheet **10_4_19.** The data for a Single Line is in C1 and the data for
Multiple Lines is in C2. Test the nurse's claim that wait times have less
variability when there is a single line. The problem confirms that the data is
normally distributed. To perform the test, click on **Stat→ Basic Statistics → 2
Variances.** Since it is suspected that multiple lines will have the larger variance,
you should use the data for Multiple Lines as the first dataset. Select **Samples in
different columns** and enter C2 for the **First** and C1 for the **Second.**

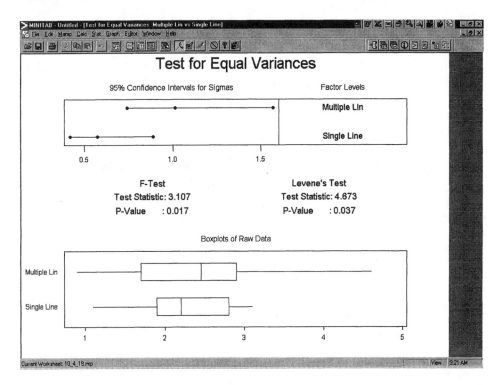

The F-statistic is 3.107 and the p-value is .017, but since you wanted an upper-
tailed test, the p-value would be .0085 and you would Reject the null hypothesis
at α=.05. Thus, there is evidence to conclude that a single line has less
variability in wait times than multiple lines. Notice that the boxplots are already
produced in the window above.

Chi-Square Procedures

Section 11.1

▶ Example 3 (pg. 660) The Chi-Square Goodness-of-Fit Test

Enter the data from Table 3 on page 660 of the textbook into the MINITAB Data
Window. Enter the Day of the Week into C1 and name it Day. Enter the
frequencies into C2 and name it Observed. Enter the distribution (from the null
hypothesis) into C3 and name it Distribution. These values should be
proportions, not fractions. Thus, 1/7 should be entered as 0.1429.

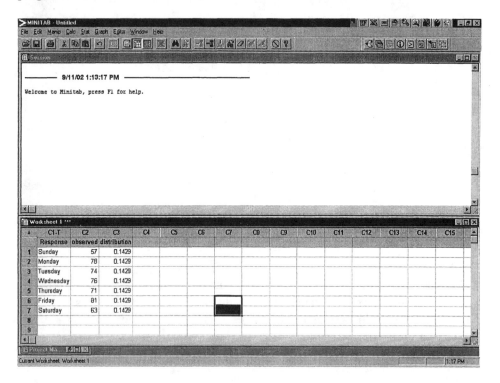

To calculate the expected frequencies, you will multiply the distribution times the
sample size, which is 500 in this example. Click on **Calc→ Calculator.** You
will **Store the result in** C4, and calculate the **Expression** C3*500. Click on **OK.**
Name C4 Expected since it now contains the expected frequencies.

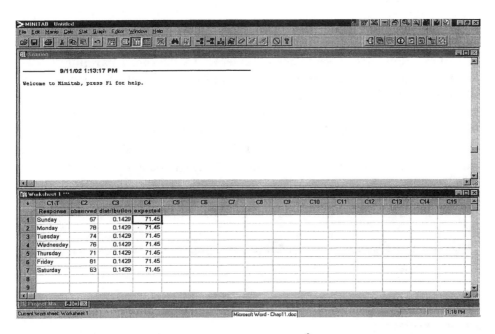

Next, calculate the chi-square test statistic, $(O - E)^2 / E$. Click on **Calc →
Calculator.** You will **Store the result in** C5, and calculate the **Expression** (C2 -
C4)**2 / C4. Click on **OK** and C5 should contain the calculated values.

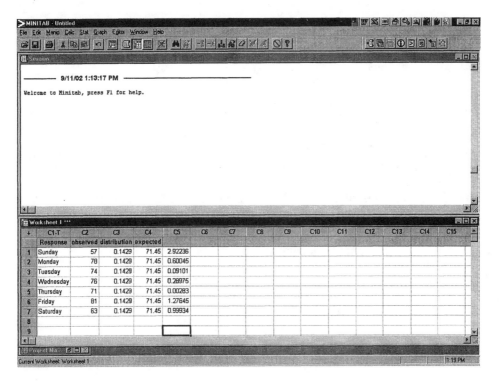

Now, just add up the values in C5 and the sum is the test statistic. Click on **Calc → Column Statistics.** Select **Sum** and enter C5 for the **Input Variable**. Click on **OK** and the Chi-Square test statistic will be displayed in the Session Window. In this example, the test statistic is 6.1822. Next, calculate the P-value to help you decide if you should reject the null hypothesis. Click on **Calc→ Probability Distributions → Chi-square.** Select **Cumulative Probability** and enter 6 **Degrees of Freedom.** Enter the value of the test statistic, 6.1822, for the **Input Constant.** Click on **OK** and $P(X \le 6.1822)$ will be in the Session Window.

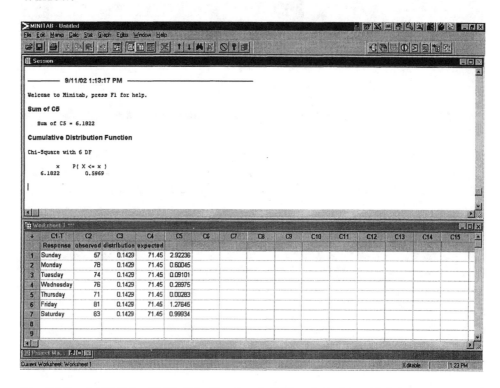

The $P(X \le 6.1822)$ is .5969. The P-value is $P(X \ge 6.1822)$, which is $1 - P(X \le 6.1822)$. This value is $1 - .5969 = .4031$. Since this P-value is larger than $\alpha = .05$, you should not reject the null hypothesis. The day on which a child is born occurs with equal frequency.

▶ Problem 7 (pg. 664)   Plain M&Ms

Enter the data into the MINITAB Data Window. Enter the Color into C1 and name it Color. Enter the frequencies into C2 and name it Observed. Enter the distribution into C3 and name it Distribution. (These values should be entered as proportions, and not percentages.) To calculate the expected frequencies, you will multiply the distribution times the sample size, which is 400 in this example. The sample size can be found by adding up the frequencies. (To do this in MINITAB, click on **Calc → Column Statistics.** Select **Sum** and enter C2 for the **Input Variable.**) Click on **Calc → Calculator.** You will **Store the result in** C4, and calculate the **Expression** C3*400. Click on **OK.** Name C4 Expected since it now contains the expected frequencies. Next, calculate the chi-square test statistic, $(O - E)^2 / E$. Click on **Calc → Calculator.** You will **Store the result in** C5, and calculate the **Expression** (C2 - C4)**2 / C4. Click on **OK** and C5 should contain the calculated values.

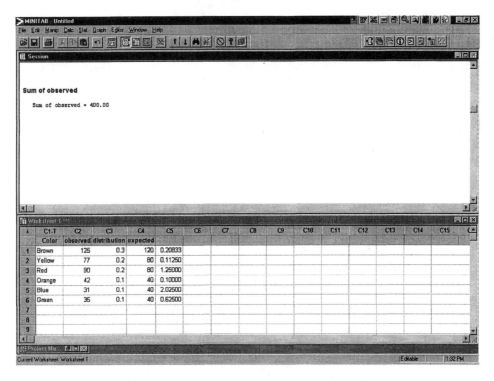

Now, just add up the values in C5 and the sum is the test statistic. Click on **Calc → Column Statistics.** Select **Sum** and enter C5 for the **Input Variable.** Click on **OK** and the Chi-Square test statistic will be displayed in the Session Window. In this example, the test statistic is 4.3208.

Next, calculate the P-value to help you decide if you should reject the null hypothesis. Click on **Calc** → **Probability Distributions** → **Chi-square.** Select **Cumulative Probability** and enter 5 **Degrees of Freedom.** Enter the value of the test statistic, 4.3208, for the **Input Constant.** When you click on **OK** , the $P(X \leq 4.3208)$ will be in the Session Window.

Sum of C5

```
Sum of C5 = 4.3208
```

Cumulative Distribution Function

```
Chi-Square with 5 DF

        x      P( X <= x )
   4.3208         0.4958
```

The P-value is $P(X \geq 4.3208) = 1 - P(X \leq 4.3208) = 1 - .4958 = .5042$. Since this P-value is so large, you would fail to reject the null hypothesis at any α-level. Thus, the distribution of colors of the M&Ms is like the manufacturer claims.

Section 11.3

▶ Example 2 (pg. 681) Chi-Square Independence Test

Enter the data from Table 16 on page 681 of the textbook into the MINITAB
Data Window. First label the columns: use Rh Level for C1, "A" for C2, "B" for
C3, "AB" for C4, and "O" for C5. Now enter the data into the appropriate
columns. Do not enter any totals.

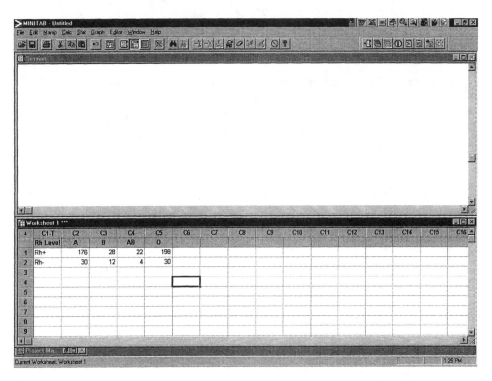

To perform the chi-square independence test, click on **Stat → Tables → Chi-
square Test.** On the input screen, select C2 - C5 for the **Columns containing
the table.** Click on **OK** and the test results will be displayed in the Session
Window.

```
Expected counts are printed below observed counts

             A         B        AB         O     Total
    1       176        28        22       198       424
          174.69     33.92     22.05    193.34

    2        30        12         4        30        76
           31.31      6.08      3.95     34.66

Total       206        40        26       228       500

Chi-Sq =  0.010 +  1.033 +  0.000 +  0.112 +
          0.055 +  5.764 +  0.001 +  0.626 = 7.601
DF = 3,  P-Value = 0.055
1 cells with expected counts less than 5.0
```

Notice that the Minitab output contains the expected frequencies below each
frequency in the table. The test statistic is Chi-Sq = 7.601 and the P-value =
.055. Since this P-value is larger than α = .05, you should not reject the null
hypothesis. Thus, there is not enough evidence to conclude that Rh-level and
blood type are related.

▶ **Problem 7 (pg. 689)** Education versus Area of Country

Open Minitab worksheet **11_3_7**. To perform the chi-square independence test, click on **Stat → Tables → Chi-square Test.** On the input screen, select C2 - C5 for the **Columns containing the table.** Click on **OK** and the test results will be displayed in the Session Window.

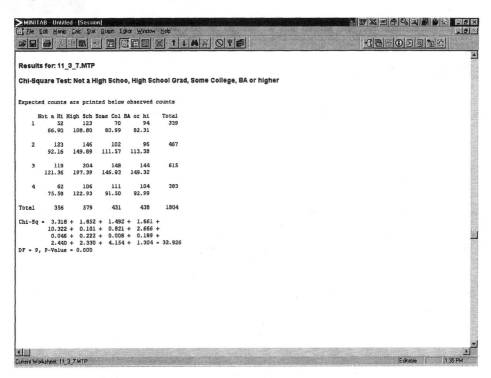

Notice that the test statistic is Chi-Sq = 32.926 and the P-value = .000. Since this P-value is smaller than α = .05, you should reject the null hypothesis. Thus, there is evidence to conclude that the level of education and region of the US are related. Notice that the Minitab output contains the expected frequencies below each frequency in the table.

Least-Squares Regression & ANOVA

Section 12.1

▶ Examples 1-5 (pg. 706-716) Least-Squares Regression

Minitab will give output for all of the first 5 examples in this section. Open worksheet **12_1_EX1.** The patients' age should be in C1, and the total cholesterol should be in C2. Notice that Age is the x-variable and Cholesterol is the y-variable. To find the regression equation, click on **Stat→ Regression → Regression.** Enter C2 for the **Response** variable, and C1 as the **Predictor.**

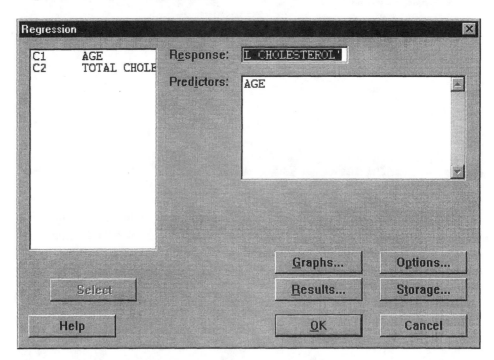

Click on **Results.** Select **Regression equation, table of coefficients, s, R-squared, and basic analysis of variance.**

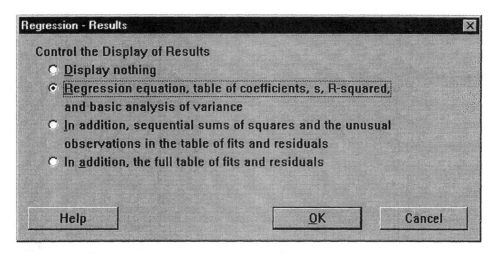

Click on **OK** to return to the main Regression Window, and now select **Graphs.**
Select **Normal plot of residuals** and enter Age beneath **Residuals versus the
variables.**

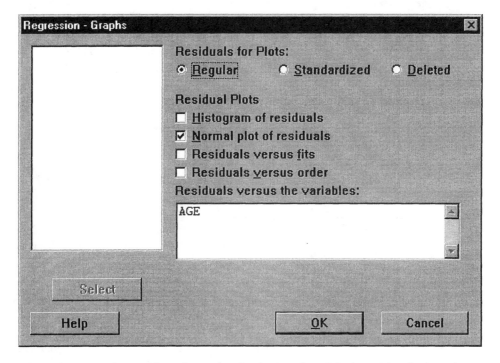

Click on **OK** twice to view the output in the Session Window. First look at the
two graphs created by Minitab.

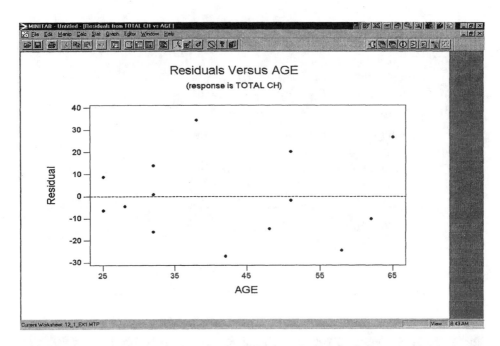

This is the plot showing the residuals plotted against the predictor variable, age. The errors are evenly spread out around the horizontal line at 0. Thus the assumption of constant error variance is satisfied. (Example 4)
Now look at the normal probability plot of the residuals. Notice that the points fall in a straight line. Thus the assumption of normality is satisfied. (Example 3)

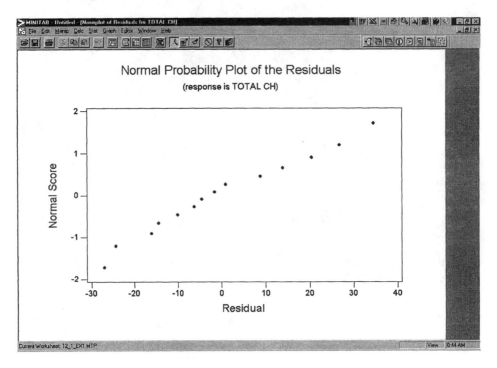

Finally, look at the results in the Session Window.

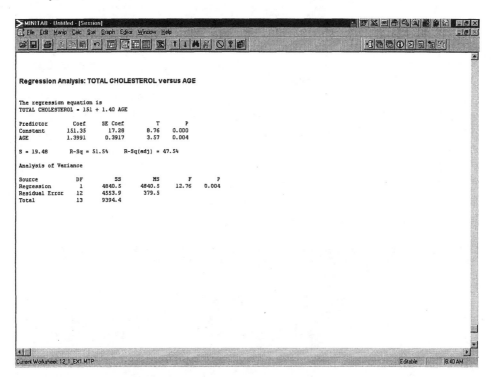

Notice that the regression equation is Total Cholesterol = 151 + 1.40 * Age.
(Example 1) The standard error is also shown, S=19.48. (Example 2) Notice
also that the t-value is shown to test the linear relationship between Age and
Cholesterol, T=3.57 with a p-value of .004. Thus, we reject the null hypothesis
and conclude that there is evidence to support the claim of a linear relationship
between age and total cholesterol level. (Example 4)

To construct the confidence interval for the slope of the regression line, use a
hand-calculator and the Minitab output. From the output in the Session Window,
you can see that b_1 is 1.3991 and you also know its standard error is .3917.
Simply look up the t-value in a table (2.179), and calculate 1.3991 ± 2.179 *
.3917. Your confidence interval is (.545, 2.253).

▶ Problem 11 (pg. 720) Cisco Systems vs. S&P 500

Open worksheet **12_1_11**. The S&P rate of return should be in C2, and Cisco Systems' rate of return should be in C3. Notice that S&P rate of return is the x-variable and Cisco Systems is the y-variable. To find the regression equation, click on **Stat → Regression → Regression.** Enter C3 for the **Response** variable, and C2 as the **Predictor.** Click on **Results.** Select **Regression equation, table of coefficients, s, R-squared, and basic analysis of variance.** Click on **OK** to return to the main Regression Window, and now select **Graphs.** Select **Normal plot of residuals** and enter C2 beneath **Residuals versus the variables.** In this problem, you also want to find the mean rate of return for Cisco Systems stock if the rate of return of the S&P 500 is 4.2 percent. Click on **Options** and enter 4.2 beneath **Prediction intervals for new observations.**

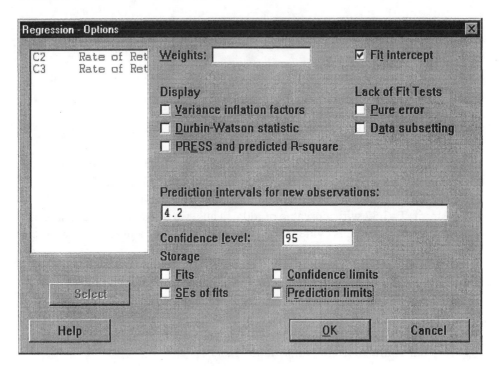

Click on **OK** twice to view the output in the Session Window.

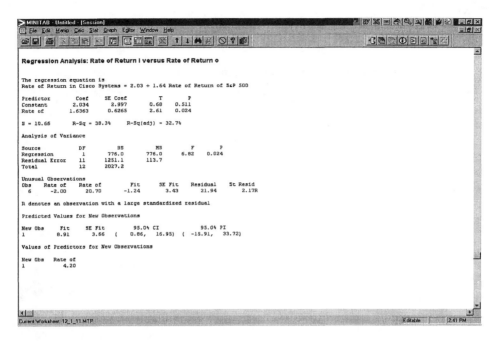

The regression equation is Rate of Return in Cisco Systems = 2.03 + 1.64 * Rate of Return of S&P 500. Thus, the unbiased estimates of β_0 and β_1 are 2.03 and 1.64. The standard error is S=10.66. To determine if the residuals are normally distributed with constant error variance, examine the two plots.

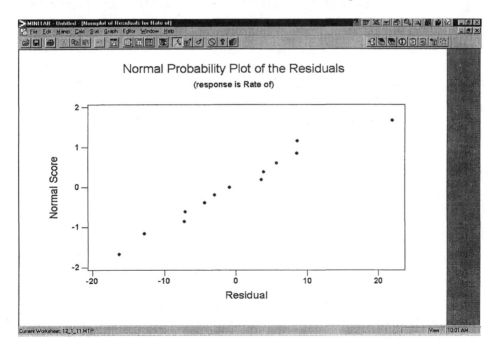

Since the normal probability plot is very linear, the residuals are approximately normal. From the output, the standard error of the S&P Rate of Return is .6265.

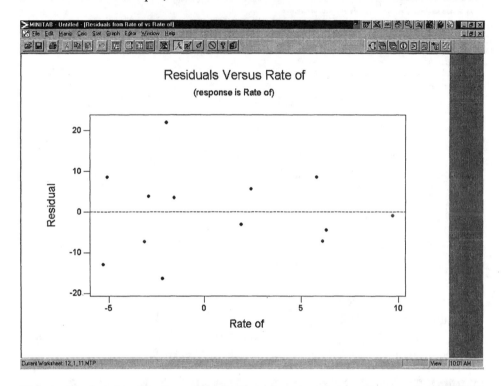

This is the plot showing the residuals plotted against the predictor variable, S&P Rate of Return. The errors are evenly spread out around the horizontal line at 0. Thus the assumption of constant error variance is satisfied. The t-value to test if a linear relation exists between the S&P rate of return and the Cisco Systems rate of return is T=2.61 with a p-value of .024 (shown on the previous page in the Session Window output). Since .024 is smaller than α=.10, you would reject the null hypothesis and conclude that there is a linear relationship.

To construct the confidence interval for the slope of the regression line, use a hand-calculator and the Minitab output. You know that b_1 is 1.6363 and you also know its standard error is .6265. Simply look up the t-value in a table ($t_{.005,11}$ = 3.106), and calculate $1.6363 \pm 3.106 * .6265$. Your confidence interval is (-.31, 3.58).

To find the mean rate of return for Cisco Systems stock if the rate of return of the S&P 500 is 4.2 percent, look at the output in the Session Window. Near the bottom, beneath **Predicted values for new observations**, the value for "Fit" is 8.91. This is the estimate of rate of return for Cisco Systems when the rate of return for the S&P 500 is 4.2 percent.

Section 12.2

▶ Examples 1&2 (pg. 725) Confidence and Prediction Intervals

Open worksheet **12_1_EX1**. The patients' age should be in C1, and the total cholesterol should be in C2. Notice that Age is the x-variable and Cholesterol is the y-variable. To find the regression equation, click on **Stat→ Regression →Regression.** Enter C2 for the **Response** variable, and C1 as the **Predictor.** Click on **Options.** Enter 42 below **Prediction intervals for new observations**, and then enter 95 for **Confidence level.** Be sure to select both **Confidence limits** and **prediction limits.**

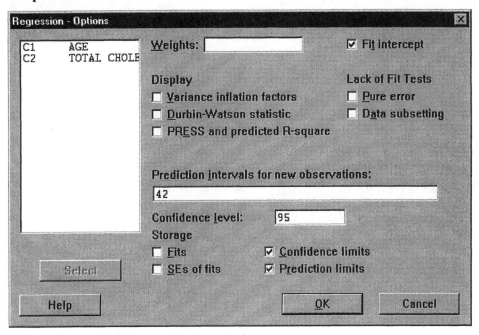

Click on **OK** twice to view the output in the Session Window.

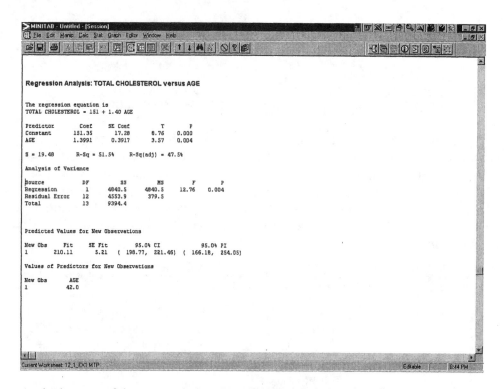

At the bottom of the screen, below "Predicted Values for New Observations", there is the heading "Fit". The 210.11 is the predicted cholesterol level for a 42 year old. The confidence interval and prediction intervals are also shown.

▶ **Problem 5 (pg. 727)** Height vs. Head Circumference

Open worksheet **12_1_7.** Height is in C1 and Head Circumference is in C2. Predict the mean head circumference of children who are 25.75 inches tall, and construct 95% confidence and prediction intervals. First, find the regression equation. Click on **Stat → Regression → Regression.** Enter C2 for the **Response** variable, and C1 as the **Predictor.** Click on **Results.** Select **Regression equation, table of coefficients, s, R-squared, and basic analysis of variance.** Click on **Options.** Enter 25.75 below **Prediction intervals for new observations,** and then enter 95 for **Confidence level.** Be sure to select both **Confidence limits** and **prediction limits.** Click on **OK** twice.

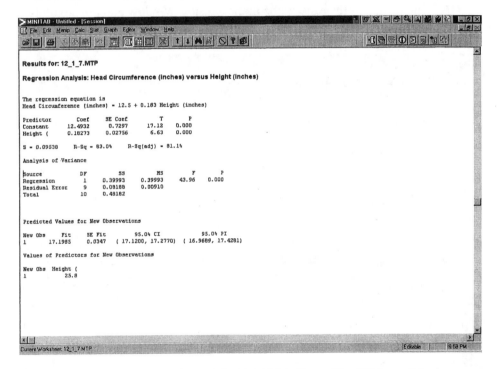

The predicted head circumference is 17.1985 inches. The 95% confidence interval is (17.12, 17.277) and the 95% prediction interval is (16.9689, 17.4281).

Section 12.3

> ▶ Problem 5 (pg. 742) Reaction Time

Open worksheet **12_3_5.** The data for the three study groups should be in C1, C2, and C3. First verify that the data is approximately normal. Click on **Graph** → **Probability Plot.** Enter C1 for the **Variable**, be sure that the **Distribution** is Normal, and click on **OK**. Repeat this for C2 and C3. To perform a one-way analysis of variance, click on **Stat** → **ANOVA** → **One Way (Unstacked)**. Select all three columns and click on **Graphs.** Select **Boxplots of data.** Click on **OK.** The results of the test will be in the Session Window and the boxplots will be in the Graph Window.

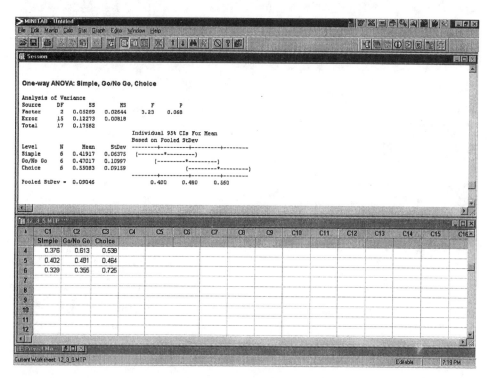

Notice that the F=3.23 with a p-value of .068. Since this is larger than α=.05, do not reject the null hypothesis. The evidence supports theory that the mean reaction time of the three groups is equal. The confidence intervals for the means are pictured in the Session Window. Notice that the intervals overlap, thus supporting the conclusion of the test -- that the means are equal. . Next, look at the boxplots of the three study groups.

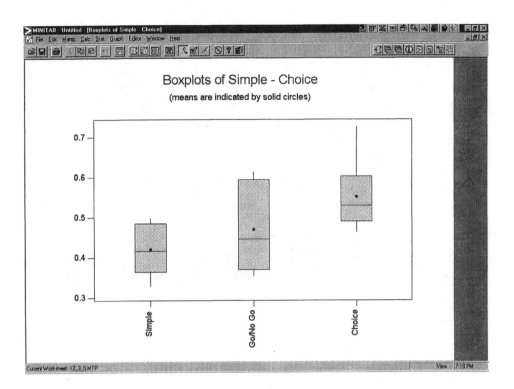

These boxplots show that the means of the three study groups are similar.

> **Problem 7 (pg. 743)** Crash Data

Open worksheet **12_3_7.** The chest compression data for the three different classes of vehicles should be in C2, C4, and C6. First verify that the data is approximately normal. Click on **Graph → Probability Plot.** Enter C2 for the **Variable**, be sure that the **Distribution** is Normal, and click on **OK.** Repeat this for C4 and C6. To perform a one-way analysis of variance, click on **Stat → ANOVA → One Way (Unstacked).** Select all three columns (C2, C4, and C6), and click on **Graphs.** Select **Boxplots of data.** Click on **OK.** The results of the test will be in the Session Window and the boxplots will be in the Graph Window.

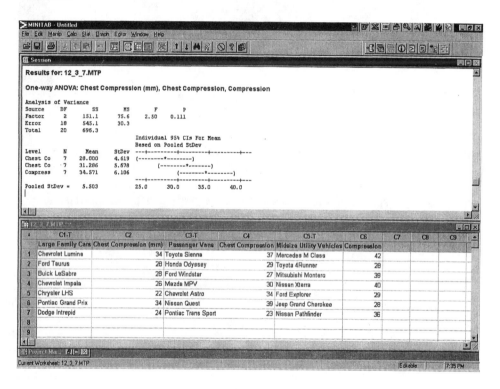

The test statistic is F=2.50. Since the p-value is .111 and is larger than α=.01, do not reject the null hypothesis. The evidence supports theory that the mean chest compression for the three vehicle types is equal. The picture of the confidence intervals shows that the three intervals overlap, supporting the conclusion of the test. The boxplots also confirm the result.

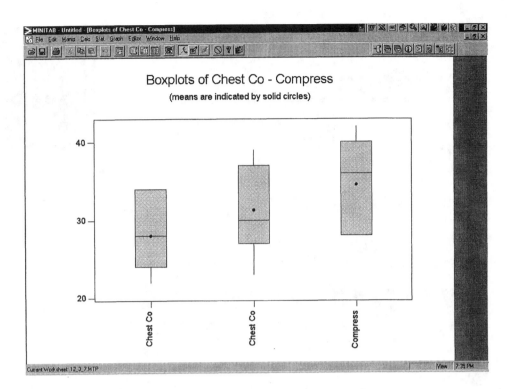

The mean chest compression for the three vehicle types is very similar.

Nonparametric Statistics

CHAPTER

13

Section 13.2

▶ Example 3 (pg. 763) Testing for Randomness (Small Sample)

Enter the data into C1 in a Minitab Worksheet. Minitab is expecting numerical data, so use a 0=Male and 1=Female (coded below in C2).

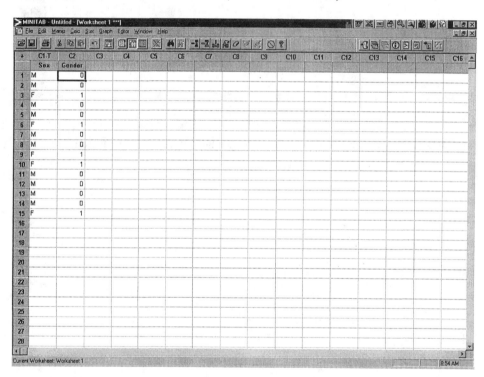

Click on **Stat → Nonparametrics → Runs Test.** Select C2 as the **Variable.** Since the data is 1s and 0s, it is binomial data. Select **Above and below .5.**

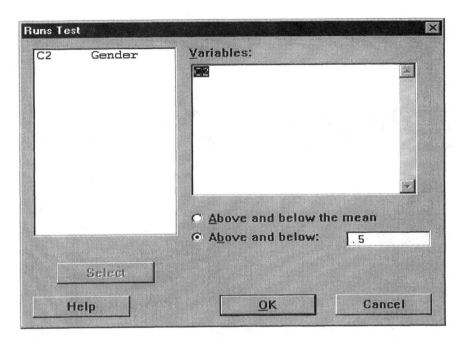

Click on **OK** and the results will be in the Session Window.

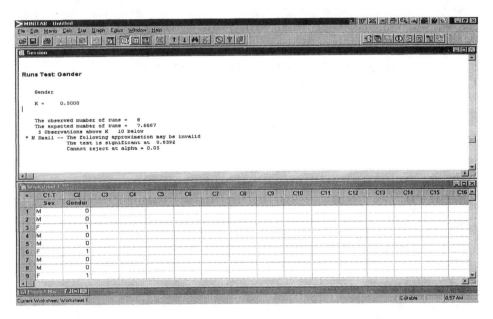

Notice that the P-value = .8392. Since this value is larger than α=.05, you would not reject the null hypothesis. Thus, students enter the room in a random order as it pertains to gender.

▶ Problem 5 (pg. 765) Baseball

Enter the data into C1 in a Minitab Worksheet. Minitab is expecting numerical data, so use a 0=Fastball and 1=Change-up.

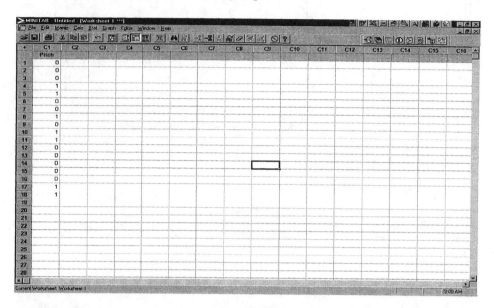

Click on **Stat → Nonparametrics → Runs Test.** Select C1 as the **Variable.** Since the data is 1s and 0s, it is binomial data. Select **Above and below .5.** Click on **OK** and the results will be in the Session Window.

Runs Test: Pitch

```
    Pitch
    K =      0.5000


    The observed number of runs =    8
    The expected number of runs =    9.5556
     7 Observations above K    11 below
 * N Small -- The following approximation may be invalid
            The test is significant at   0.4250
            Cannot reject at alpha = 0.05
```

Notice that the P-value = .4250. Since this value is larger than α=.05, you would not reject the null hypothesis. Thus, Keith Foulke chooses his pitches randomly.

Section 13.3

▶ Example 1 (pg. 771)   One-sample Sign Test

Enter the data into C1 in the MINITAB Data Window. (Do not type in the $ sign.) To perform the Sign Test, click on **Stat → Nonparametrics → 1-sample Sign.** Select C1 as the **Variable.** Since you would like to test if the median amount of credit card debt is $500, enter 500 for **Test median** and select **not equal** for the **Alternative.**

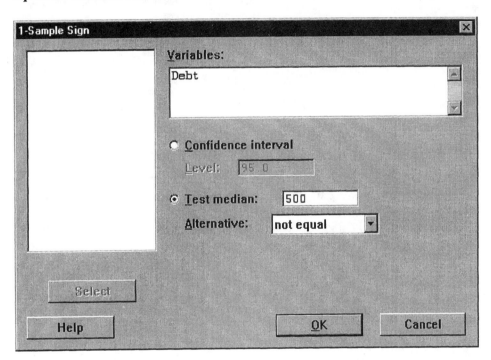

Click on **OK** and the results will be displayed in the Session Window.

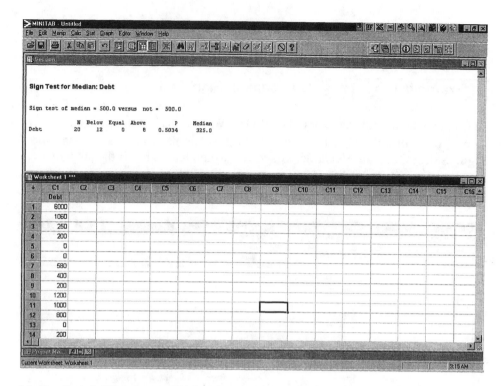

Notice that the P-value = .5034. Since this is such a large P-value, you would fail to reject the null hypothesis. Thus, there is no evidence that the median amount of credit card debt is different from $500.

▶ Problem 7 (pg. 774) Acid Rain

Open worksheet **13_3_7**. The pH levels are in C1 of the MINITAB Data
Window. Now perform a 1-sample Sign test. Click on **Stat → Nonparametrics
→ 1-sample Sign**. Select C1 as the **Variable**. Since you would like to test if the
pH level is more than 4.90, enter 4.9 for **Test median** and select **greater than** for
the **Alternative**. Click on **OK**.

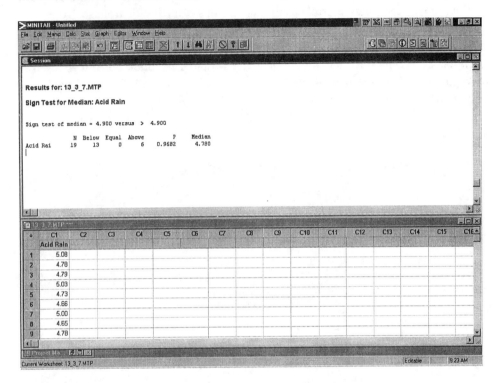

Notice that the P-value = .9682. Since this value is larger than α=.05, you would
fail to reject the null hypothesis. Thus, there is not enough evidence to conclude
that the pH level of rain has increased since 1990.

Section 13.4

▶ Example 1 (pg. 779) Performing a Wilcoxon Signed-Rank Test

Enter the data in a Minitab Worksheet. Enter the Nortel Networks data in C1 and
the JDS Uniphase data in C2. Since the claim is that the median volume of JDS
Uniphase is greater than Nortel's, subtract Nortel's from JDS Uniphase. To
calculate the differences, click **Calc → Calculator. Store the result in variable**
C3 and calculate the **Expression** C2-C1. Click on **OK** and C3 should contain the
differences. To perform the Wilcoxon Signed Rank Test, click on **Stat →**
Nonparametrics → 1-sample Wilcoxon. You should use C3 for the **Variable.**
Since you are using the differences in this example, you want to compare the
median difference to 0. So, enter 0 for **Test Median** and choose **greater than** as
the **Alternative.**

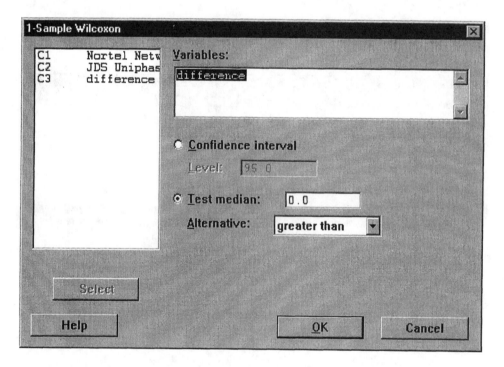

Click on **OK** to view the results of the test in the Session Window.

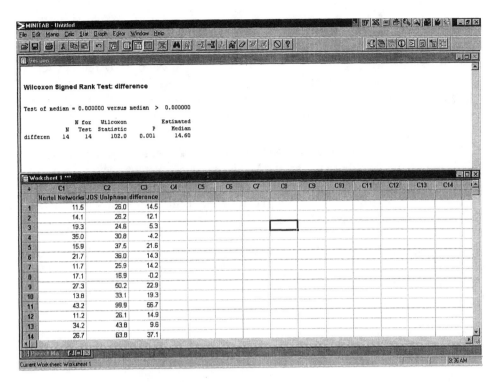

The MINITAB output tells you that the Wilcoxon Statistic is 102 and the P-value is .001. The important thing to notice is that the P-value = .001. Since this is smaller than α = .05, you would reject the null hypothesis. Thus, there is sufficient evidence to say that the median volume of JDS Uniphase is greater than Nortel Network's median volume.

▶ Problem 15 (pg. 784) Car Rentals

Open worksheet **13_4_15.** Thrifty rental rates are in C2 and Hertz rental rates are in C3. Since the claim is that the Thrifty charges less than Hertz, subtract Thrifty rates from Hertz rates. To calculate the differences, click **Calc→ Calculator. Store the result in variable** C4 and calculate the **Expression** C3-C2. Click on **OK** and C4 should contain the differences. To perform the Wilcoxon Signed Rank Test, click on **Stat → Nonparametrics → 1-sample Wilcoxon.** You should use C4 for the **Variable.** Since you are using the differences in this example, you want to compare the median difference to 0. So, enter 0 for **Test Median** and choose **greater than** as the **Alternative.** Click on **OK** and the results will be in the Session Window.

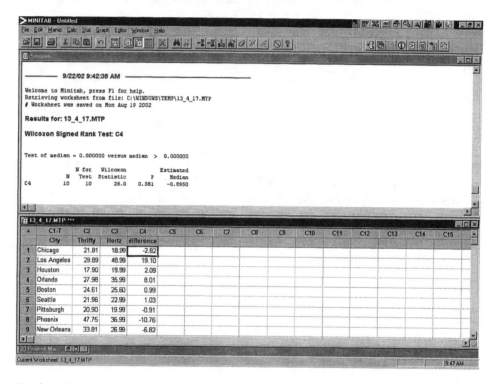

Look at the results carefully. The P-value is .581. The Wilcoxon statistic is 26. In this example, since the P-value is larger than α=.05, you would fail to reject the null hypothesis. Thus, there is no evidence that Thrifty charges less than Hertz.

Section 13.5

▶ Example 1 (pg. 790) Mann-Whitney Test

Enter the data in a Minitab worksheet. Enter the data for Ill people into C1 and for Healthy people into C2. Click on **Stat → Nonparametrics → Mann-Whitney.** Enter C1 for the **First Sample,** C2 for the **Second Sample**, and select **greater than** as the **Alternative** since you want to see if the titer level in the ill group is greater than the level in the healthy group.

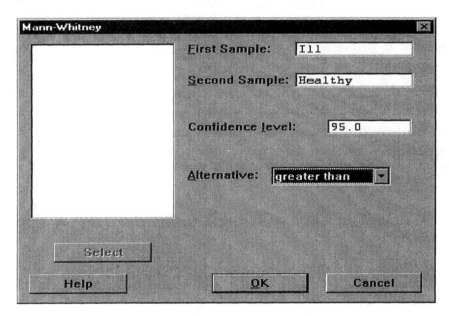

Click on **OK**. The results should be in the Session Window.

Mann-Whitney Test and CI: Ill, Healthy

```
Ill        N =  11    Median =        640.0
Healthy    N =  11    Median =        320.0
Point estimate for ETA1-ETA2 is        320.0
95.1 Percent CI for ETA1-ETA2 is (-0.0,559.9)
W = 152.0
Test of ETA1 = ETA2  vs  ETA1 > ETA2 is significant at 0.0503
The test is significant at 0.0466 (adjusted for ties)
```

Since the P-value = .0503 and is smaller than α=.10, you would reject the null hypothesis. There is evidence to conclude ill people have a greater titer level than healthy people.

> ▶ Problem 9 (pg. 795) Housing Prices

Open worksheet **13_5_9.** Denver housing prices are in C1 and Chicago prices are in C2. Click on **Stat → Nonparametrics → Mann-Whitney.** Enter C1 for the **First Sample,** C2 for the **Second Sample**, and select **not equal** as the **Alternative** since you want to test the claim that the average price in the two cities is different. Click on **OK**. The results should be in the Session Window.

Mann-Whitney Test and CI: Denver, Chicago

```
Denver     N =  17     Median =      189900
Chicago    N =  14     Median =      161000
Point estimate for ETA1-ETA2 is      38900
95.1 Percent CI for ETA1-ETA2 is (-38500,107700)
W = 300.0
Test of ETA1 = ETA2  vs  ETA1 not = ETA2 is significant at 0.2750

Cannot reject at alpha = 0.05
```

Since the P-value = .2750 and is larger than α=.05, you would fail to reject the null hypothesis. There is no evidence to conclude the average price of housing in Denver is different than the average price in Chicago.

Section 13.6

▶ Example 1 (pg. 800) The Spearman Rank Correlation
Coefficient

Enter the data into the MINITAB Data Window. Enter the Per Capita GDP into
C1 and the Life Expectancy into C2. To rank the data values, click on **Manip** →
Rank. On the input screen, you should **Rank data in** C1 and **Store ranks in** C3.
When you click on **OK**, the ranks of the Per Capita GDP should be in C3.

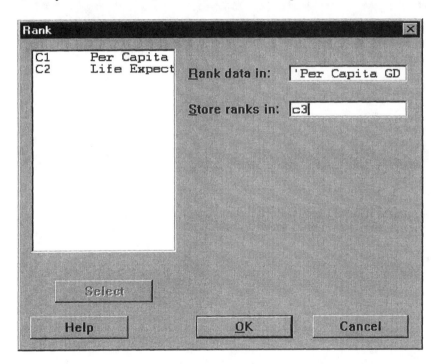

Repeat this using the Life Expectancies and storing the ranks in C4. Now you
should have the ranks of the data in C3 and C4.

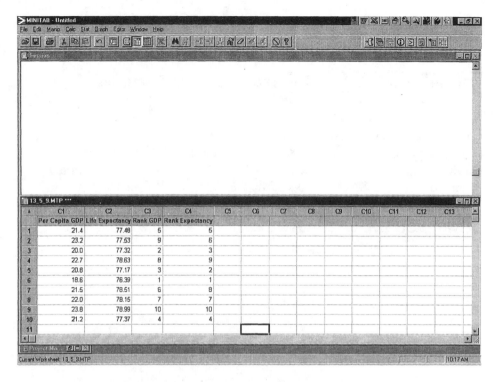

To calculate Spearman's Rank Correlation Coefficient, simply use Pearson's correlation on the ranks of the data. Click on **Stat**→ **Basic Statistics** → **Correlation.** Enter C3 and C4 for the **Variables** and select **Display p-values.**

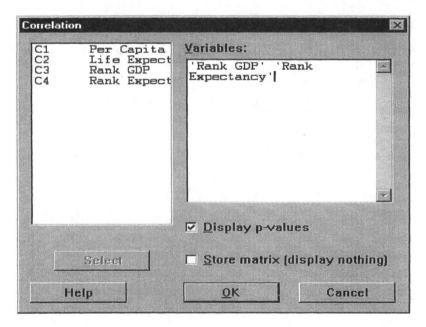

When you click on **OK**, the results will be displayed in the Session Window.

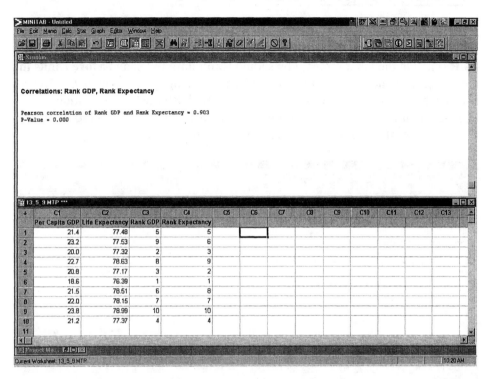

In this example, notice that the Spearman's Rank Correlation Coefficient is .903 and the P-value is .000. Since this P-value is smaller than $\alpha = .05$, you would reject the null hypothesis. Thus, you can conclude that there is a significant correlation between Per Capita GDP and Life Expectancy.

▶ Problem 5 (pg. 803) Income vs. Education

Open worksheet **13_6_5.** The percentage of the population with a college degree is in C2 and the personal income is in C3. First, rank the data. Click on **Manip → Rank.** On the input screen, you should **Rank data in** C2 and **Store ranks in** C4. When you click on **OK,** the ranks of the Percentages should be in C4. Repeat this for the Income and **store ranks in** C5. Now, calculate the correlation coefficient of the ranks. Click on **Stat → Basic Statistics → Correlation.** Enter C4 and C5 for the **Variables** and select **Display p-values.**

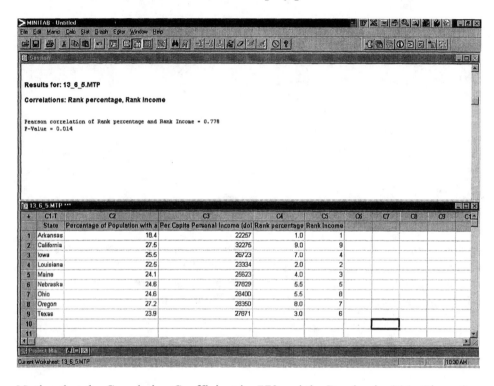

Notice that the Correlation Coefficient is .778 and the P-value is .014. Since the P-value is smaller than α=.05, you would reject the null hypothesis. Thus, there is a significant correlation between Education and Income.

Section 13.7

▶ **Example 1 (pg. 807)** Performing a Kruskal-Wallis Test

Enter the data in a Minitab worksheet. First draw side-by-side boxplots of the 3
sets of data. To do this, click on **Graph → Boxplot.** Select C1, C2, and C3 for
Graphs 1, 2, and 3 beneath **Y** variable. Click on **Options** and select **Transpose
X and Y.** Click on **Frame → Multiple graphs.** Select **Overlay graphs on
same page.** Click on **OK** twice to view the boxplots.

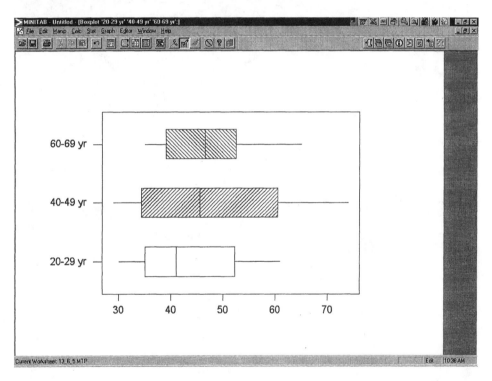

To perform a Kruskal-Wallis test, MINITAB requires that the data be stacked
into one column with a second column identifying which sample each data value
came from. To do this, click on **Manip → Stack → Stack Columns.** Select all
three columns to be stacked on top of each other. Select **Column of current
worksheet** and enter C4 and **Store subscripts in** C5. The subscripts will be
numbers 1, 2, or 3 to indicate which column the data value came from. Be sure
that **Use variable names in subscript column** is NOT selected.

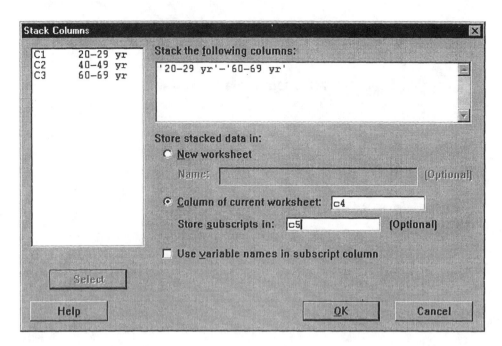

Click on **OK.** Name C4 HDL levels and C5 Age group. Notice that in C5, 1 represents 20-29 yr. olds, 2 represents 40-49 yr. olds, and 3 represents 60-69 yr. olds.

Now, to do the Kruskal-Wallis test, click on **Stat → Nonparametrics →**
Kruskal-Wallis. The **Response** variable is HDL level (C4) and the **Factor** is
Age group (C5).

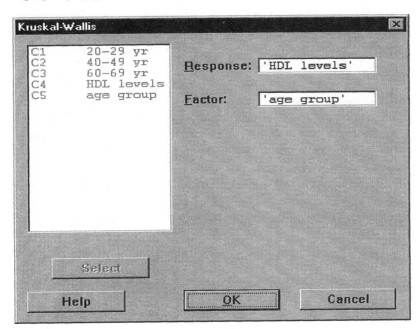

Click on **OK** and the results will be displayed in the Session Window.

Kruskal-Wallis Test: HDL levels versus age group

```
Kruskal-Wallis Test on HDL leve

age grou     N     Median     Ave Rank          Z
1           12      41.00         16.2      -0.92
2           12      45.50         18.8       0.12
3           12      46.50         20.5       0.81
Overall     36                    18.5

H = 1.01   DF = 2   P = 0.604
H = 1.01   DF = 2   P = 0.603 (adjusted for ties)
```

Notice that the test statistic is H=1.01 and the P-value=.604. With such a large
P-value, you do not reject the null hypothesis. So, there is a no difference in the
distribution of HDL levels for the three age groups.

> ▶ Problem 5 (pg. 811) Corn Production

Open worksheet **13_7_5.** The data should be in C1 - C5. First draw the boxplots
of the data. To do this, click on **Graph → Boxplot.** Select C1 - C5 for Graphs 1,
2, 3, 4 and 5 beneath **Y** variable. Click on **Options** and select **Transpose X and
Y.** Click on **Frame → Multiple graphs.** Select **Overlay graphs on same page.**
Click on **OK** twice to view the boxplots. To perform a Kruskal-Wallis test,
MINITAB requires that the data be stacked into one column with a second
column identifying which sample each data value came from. To do this, click
on **Manip → Stack → Stack Columns.** Select all five columns to be stacked on
top of each other. Select **Column of current worksheet** and enter C6 and **Store
subscripts in** C7. The subscripts will be numbers 1, 2, 3, 4 or 5 to indicate
which column the data value came from. Be sure that **Use variable names in
subscript column** is NOT selected. Click on **OK.** Name C6 Plants and C7 Plot
Type. Notice that in C7, 1 represents Sludge Plot, 2 represents Spring Disk, etc.
Now, to do the Kruskal-Wallis test, click on **Stat → Nonparametrics →
Kruskal-Wallis.** The **Response** variable is Plants (C6) and the **Factor** is Plot
Type (C7). Click on **OK** and the results will be displayed in the Session Window.

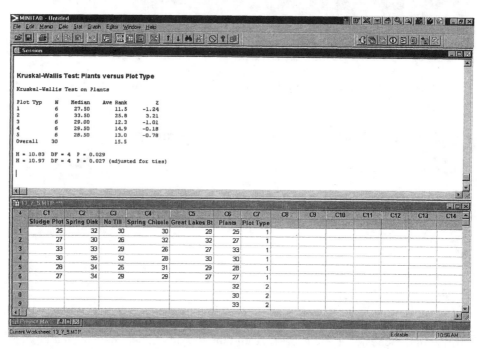

Notice that the test statistic is H=10.83 and the P-value=.029. Since this P-value
is smaller than α=.05, you should reject the null hypothesis. So, there is a
difference in the distribution for each type of plot.

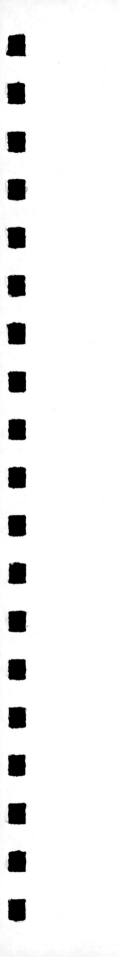